SCHOLASTIC

Maths Practice for

Year 3

Ages 7–8

This book belongs to:

Maths Year 3, Book 1

Scholastic Education, an imprint of Scholastic Ltd
Book End, Range Road, Witney, Oxfordshire, OX29 0YD
Registered office: Westfield Road, Southam, Warwickshire CV47 0RA
www.scholastic.co.uk

3 4 5 6 7 8 9   6 7 8 9 0 1 2 3 4 5

British Library Cataloguing-in-Publication Data
A catalogue record for this book is available from the British Library.

ISBN 978-1407-14209-8
Printed in Malaysia

Editorial
Rachel Morgan, Robin Hunt, Kate Baxter, Lesley Fletcher, Gemma Cary, Mark Walker

Design
Scholastic Design Team: Neil Salt, Nicolle Thomas and Oxford Designers & Illustrators Ltd

Cover Design
Neil Salt

Illustration
Aleksander Sotirovski

Contents

Why buy this book?

This series has been designed to support the introduction of the new National Curriculum in schools in England. The new curriculum is more challenging in mathematics and includes the requirement for children's understanding to be secure before moving on. These practice books will help your child revise and practise all of the skills they will learn at school, and including some topics they might not have encountered previously.

How to use this book

- The content is divided into National Curriculum topics (for example, Addition and subtraction, Fractions and so on). Find out what your child is doing in school and dip into the relevant practice activities as required.

- Share the activities and support your child if necessary using the helpful quick tips at the top of most pages.

- Keep the working time short and come back to an activity if your child finds it too difficult. Ask your child to note any areas of difficulty at the back of the book. Don't worry if your child does not 'get' a concept first time, as children learn at different rates and content is likely to be covered throughout the school year.

- Check your child's answers using the answers section at the back of the book.

- Give lots of encouragement and tick off the progress chart as your child completes each chapter.

How to use the book

This tells you which topic you're working on.

This is the title of the activity.

These boxes will help you with the activity.

Multiplication and division

Multiply using teen numbers

Practise saying the 2-, 3-, 4-, 5-, 8- and 10-times tables.
To multiply by a 'teen' number, partition the number.
For example, 4 × 16, work out 4 × 10 (**40**) and 4 × 6 (**24**) and then add them: **40** + **24** = 64.

Complete the table.

1. Choose a number from the grid.
2. Choose a number from the row.
3. Multiply your grid number by your row number.
4. Do this five times using a different pair of numbers each time.

Grid numbers

11	16	19	12	14
15	18	10	13	17

Row numbers

2 3 4 5 6 10

Grid number	Row number	Number sentence	Jottings	Answer

26 MATHS YEAR 3

Multiplication and division

Tens and units multiplication

To multiply a 2-digit number by a 1-digit number, first partition the 2-digit number into 10s and 1s.
For example, for 32 × 2, partition 32 into 30 and 2.

30 × 2 = 60
2 × 2 = 4
60 + 4 = 64

1. Now try this method for these multiplication sentences.

a. 43 × 2	b. 23 × 2
c. 24 × 3	d. 48 × 2
e. 14 × 3	f. 26 × 4

MATHS YEAR 3 27

This is the instruction text. It tells you what to do.

Follow the instruction to complete the activity.

You might have to write on lines, in boxes, draw or circle things.

Measurement

Using a ruler

Practise using a ruler to measure different items. Make sure that the '0' on the ruler is lined up with the end of the item you are measuring. If the object is more than $8\frac{1}{2}$cm but not quite 9cm, then you round up the measurement to 9cm. If it is nearer to $8\frac{1}{2}$cm then you round down to $8\frac{1}{2}$cm.

1. You need a ruler marked in half centimetres. Measure the lines below (labelled a. to e.) as accurately as you can. Write down your measurements.

a. ____________

b. ____________

c. ____________

d. ____________

e. ____________

2. Now draw these lines. Be as accurate as you can.

a. 5cm
b. 3cm
c. $7\frac{1}{2}$cm
d. $1\frac{1}{2}$cm
e. $3\frac{1}{2}$cm

42 MATHS YEAR 3

Measurement

10 centimetres

Estimate and measure lengths using centimetres and half centimetres. Make sure you line up the item to be measured with the '0' on the ruler, then take a reading. When estimating, look at 10cm carefully and then try and find items that are about that length.

1. Find something at home that you estimate to be about 10cm long.
Now measure it as accurately as you can, to the nearest $\frac{1}{2}$cm use the ruler on the page to help you.
Write your estimate and measurement in the table.
Do this five more times.

I chose	My estimate	My measurement

2. Now find something that you estimate to be about 20cm in length. Measure it and write what you did here.

MATHS YEAR 3 43

If you need help, ask an adult!

Counting in 3s, 4s and 5s

Practise counting in 3s, 4s and 5s. Can you see the pattern of numbers?

1. Write a number pattern for counting in 3s.

- Decide which number from 0 to 2 you will start on.
- Continue the pattern until the boxes are all full.

2. Write a counting pattern for counting in 4s.

- Decide which number from 0 to 3 you will start on.
- Continue the pattern until the boxes are all full.

3. Write a counting pattern for counting in 5s.

- Decide which number from 0 to 4 you will start on.
- Continue the pattern until the boxes are all full.

Counting in 10s and 100s

To count in 10s, change the 10s digit. Start with 100 and count on two 10s: 120.

To count in 100s, change the 100s digit. Start with 100 and count on three 100s: 300.

1. **Start at 340. Count back five 10s.**
   a. What number do you finish on? ______________________
   b. Which digit is always the same? **100s** **10s** **1s**

2. **Now start at 657. Count back eight 10s.**
   a. What number do you finish on? ______________________
   b. Tick the digits that are the same. **100s** **10s** **1s**

3. **Start at 163. Count on nine 10s.**
   a. What number do you finish on? ______________________
   b. Which digit is always the same? **100s** **10s** **1s**

4. **Now try 248. Count on four 100s.**
   a. What number do you finish on? ______________________
   b. Which digits change? **100s** **10s** **1s**

5. **Start on 356. Count on six 100s.**
   a. What number do you finish on? ______________________
   b. Which digits change? **100s** **10s** **1s**

6. **Start at 945. Count back as far as you can in 100s without going into negative numbers?**
   a. What number do you reach? ______________________
   b. Which digits change? **100s** **10s** **1s**

Place value: 3-digit numbers

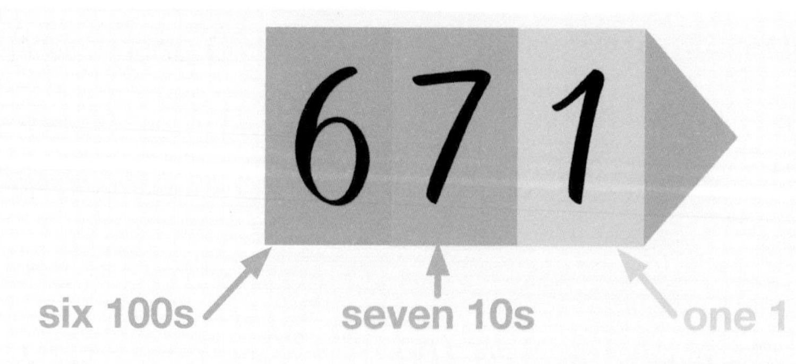

1. Write these 3-digit numbers as 100s, 10s and 1s.
   The first one has been done for you.

Number	100s	10s	1s
167	100	60	7
649			
333			
509			
590			
950			
905			
237			

2. Write four 3-digit numbers of your own in the first column of this grid.
3. Now write them in 100s, 10s and 1s.

Number	100s	10s	1s

10 more or less

Practise counting on or back in 10s from any 1- or 2-digit number.
Which digit changes each time? (10s) Which digit stays the same? (1s)
If we know 34 – 6 = 28, we can use that to work out 34 – 16 (subtract another 10) or to work out 34 – 26 (subtract two more 10s).

1. Write the answers to these number sentences.

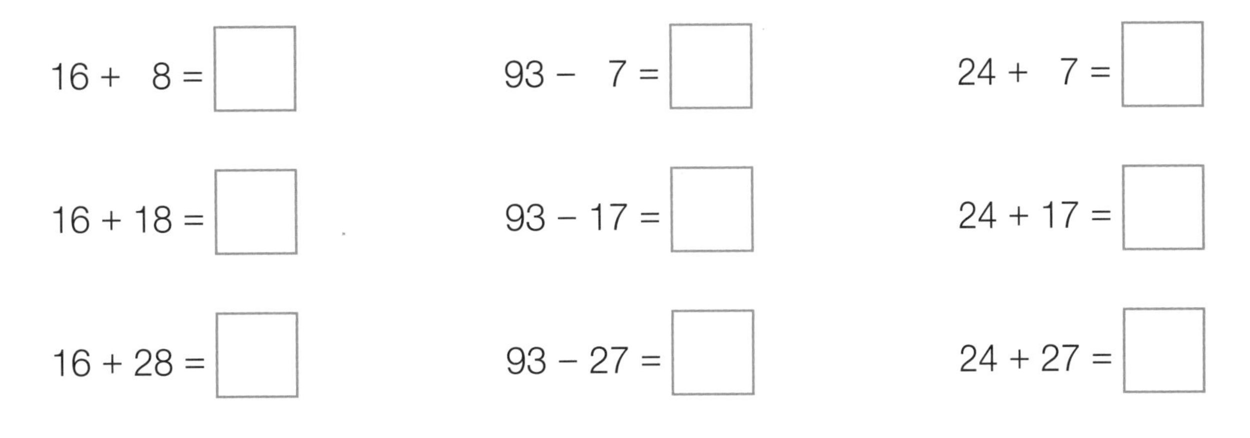

2. Continue the patterns.

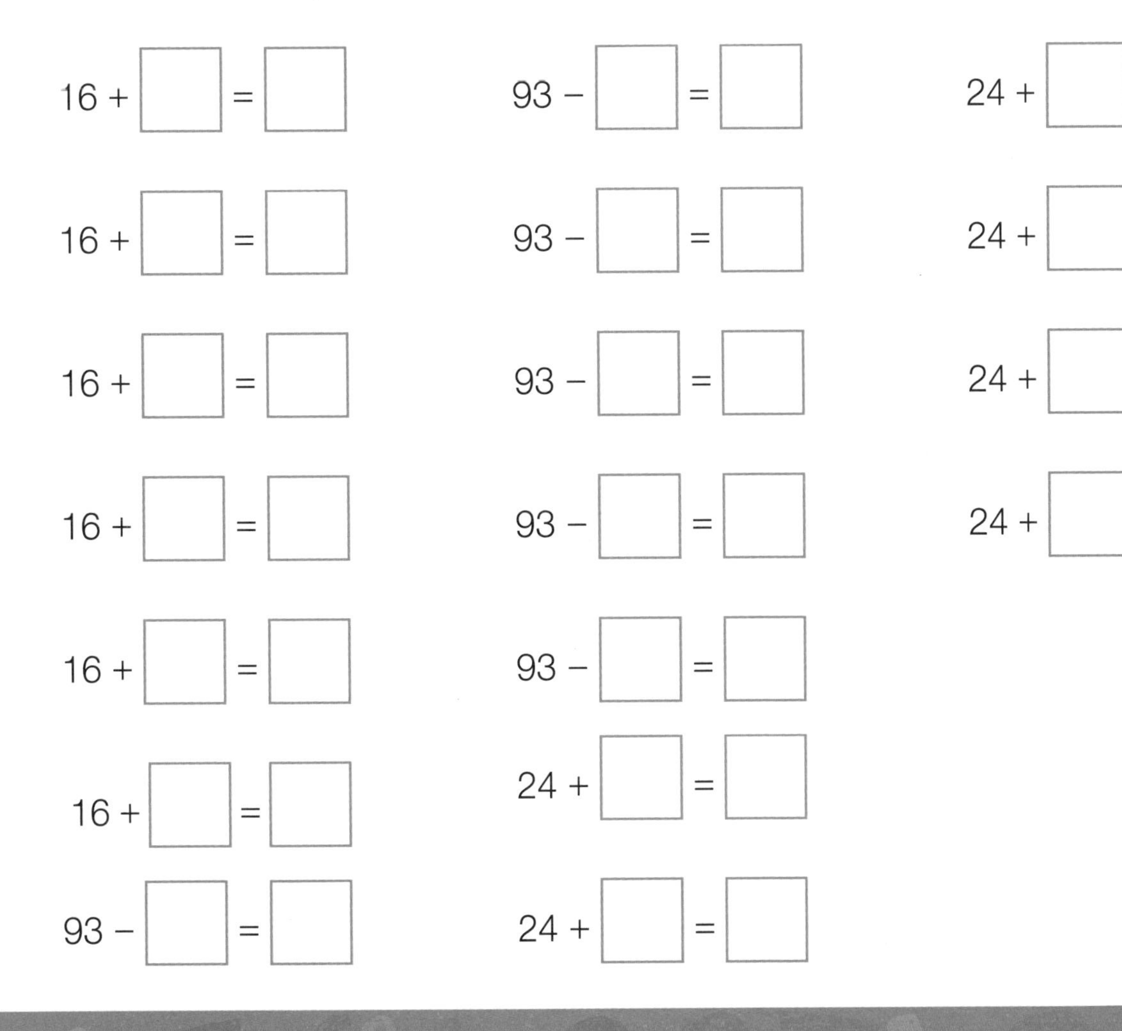

100 more or less

Practise counting on or back in 100s from any 1-, 2- or 3-digit number. Which digit changes each time?

127	**2**27	**3**27	**4**27	**5**27	**6**27

Only the 100s digit changes.

1. **Draw lines to match each number on the left with the number that is 100 more.**

18	**623**
232	**247**
147	**118**
523	**332**

2. **For each of these numbers, subtract 200 then add 200. Write your answers in the boxes.**

200 less ←	Starting number →	200 more
	362	
	759	
	594	
	831	

Number order

To put a group of large numbers in order, we look at the 100s digit first.

Look at this group of numbers: 235, 532, 352, 523.

Start with the 100s digits. **2**35 is the smallest number, then **3**52.
When the 100s digits are the same, move on to the 10s, then the 1s. The correct order is 235, 352, 523, 532.

1. Write these sets of numbers in order, starting with the smallest, on the empty number lines.

a. 165 156 651 615 516 561

b. 831 901 879 910 887 897

c. 501 516 499 504 497 500

2. Make four different 3-digit numbers using the digits 4, 8, 5 and 9. Write your numbers in the boxes below.

3. Write your numbers in order on the number line, starting with the smallest.

Numbers in digits and words

It is important to practise writing numbers as words. **4**27 written in words is **four hundred** and *twenty-seven*.

Write your answers below in numerals and then in words. Use these words to help you: *ten*, *twenty*, *thirty*, *forty*, *fifty*, *sixty*, *seventy*, *eighty*, *ninety*, *hundred*.

1. Akram has three cards.

a. Using all three cards, what is the largest number Akram can make?

☐ ______________________

b. What is the smallest 3-digit number he can make?

☐ ______________________

2. Akram swaps his cards for three different ones.

a. Using all three cards, what is the largest number he can make now?

☐ ______________________

b. What is the smallest 3-digit number he can make?

☐ ______________________

3. Akram now takes both sets of cards.

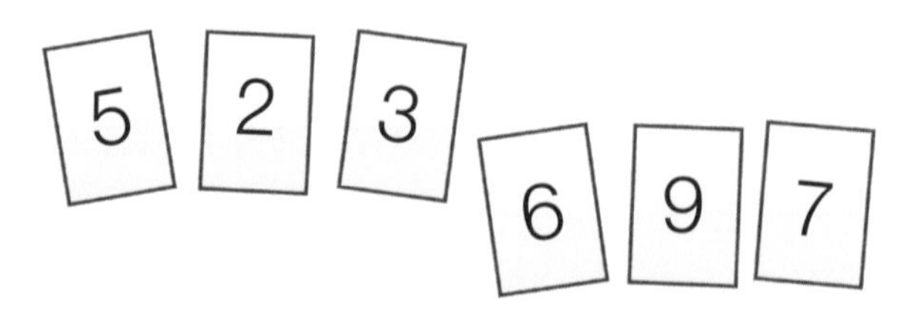

a. Using three different cards, what is the largest 3-digit number he can make?

☐ ______________________

b. What is the smallest 3-digit number he can make?

☐ ______________________

Multiples problem

Use coloured pencils to work out each pattern of multiples in the square. Then check whether numbers ending in 0 are part of the patterns. Is 10 in the multiples pattern for 2, 3, 4, 5, 8 or 10? What about the numbers 20 and 30?

1. **Is this statement true? Use the 100 square to help you decide.**

   A number ending in 0 can be in the 2-, 3-, 4-, 5-, 6- and 10-times tables.

1	2	3	4	5	6	7	8	9	10
11	12	13	14	15	16	17	18	19	20
21	22	23	24	25	26	27	28	29	30
31	32	33	34	35	36	37	38	39	40
41	42	43	44	45	46	47	48	49	50
51	52	53	54	55	56	57	58	59	60
61	62	63	64	65	66	67	68	69	70
71	72	73	74	75	76	77	78	79	80
81	82	83	84	85	86	87	88	89	90
91	92	93	94	95	96	97	98	99	100

2. **Write a sentence to explain your thinking.**

____

____

____

____

Number facts to 20

Using patterns of numbers can help you find all the facts for a number.

For 16, I can start with 0 + 16 = 16; 1 + 15 = 16; 2 + 14 = 16 and so on.

For subtraction facts I can work in the same way: 16 – 0 = 16; 16 – 1 = 15; 16 – 2 = 14 and so on.

1. Use all the numbers to 20. Find ten different ways to make the answer 17. You can make an addition or subtraction number sentence. One has been done for you.

1. 16 + 1 = 17
2. ______
3. ______
4. ______
5. ______
6. ______
7. ______
8. ______
9. ______
10. ______

2. In the box below, write as many ways as you can of making 20.

Make 100

If you know 6 + 4 = 10, you also know 60 (six 10s) + 40 (four 10s) = 100.

To work out 56 + 44, split the numbers. 50 + 40 = 90 and 6 + 4 = 10.

This makes 90 + 10 = 100.

1. Choose two numbers from the grid that total 100.
Write the addition sentence for your numbers in the boxes below.
Cross out the numbers that you chose. Repeat until all the numbers have been used.

49	8	38	11	69
16	85	36	92	78
44	89	15	84	56
22	62	31	64	51

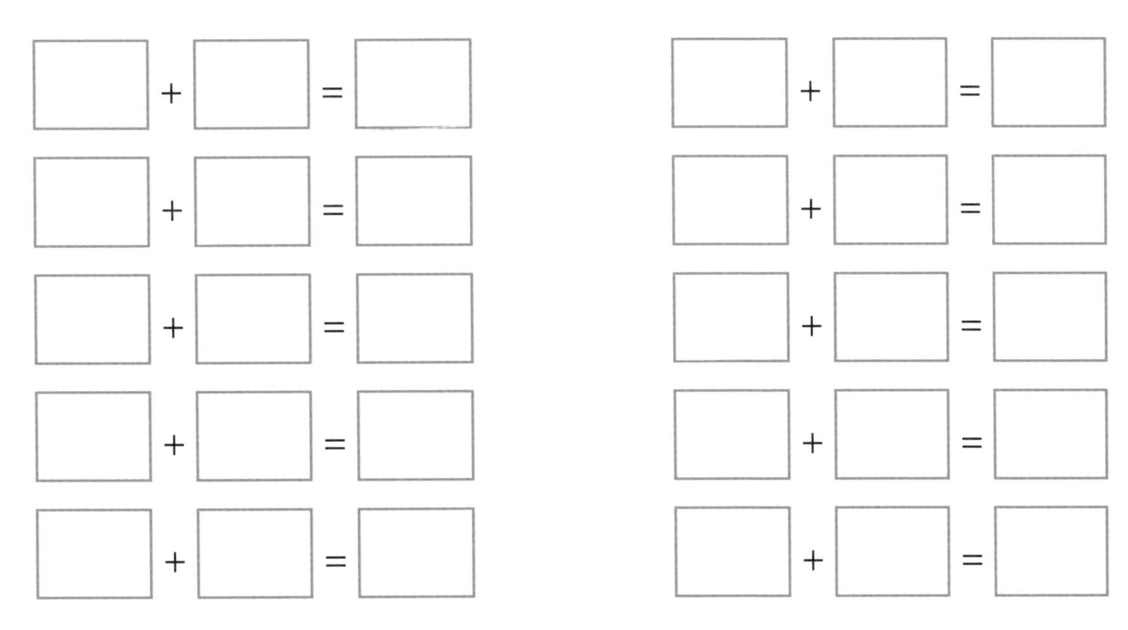

2. Write the answers to these problems.

a. Pat has saved 67 British stamps. How many more does he need to save in order to have 100 in total?

b. Clare buys two packs of sweets. The sweets cost 36p per pack. How much change will she have from £1?

Number line addition and subtraction

Number lines help to show you the steps of an addition or subtraction.

Here is 76 + 27 on a number line.

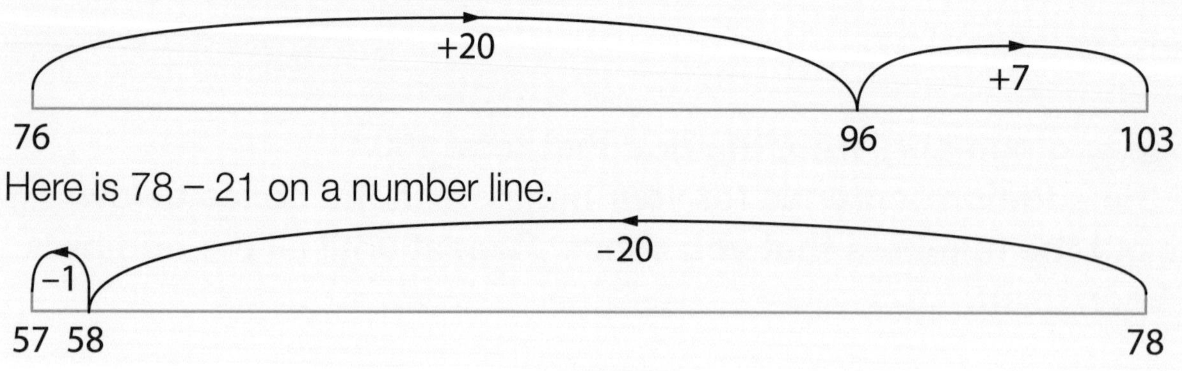

1. Use the empty number lines to help you to find the answers to these addition and subtraction sentences.

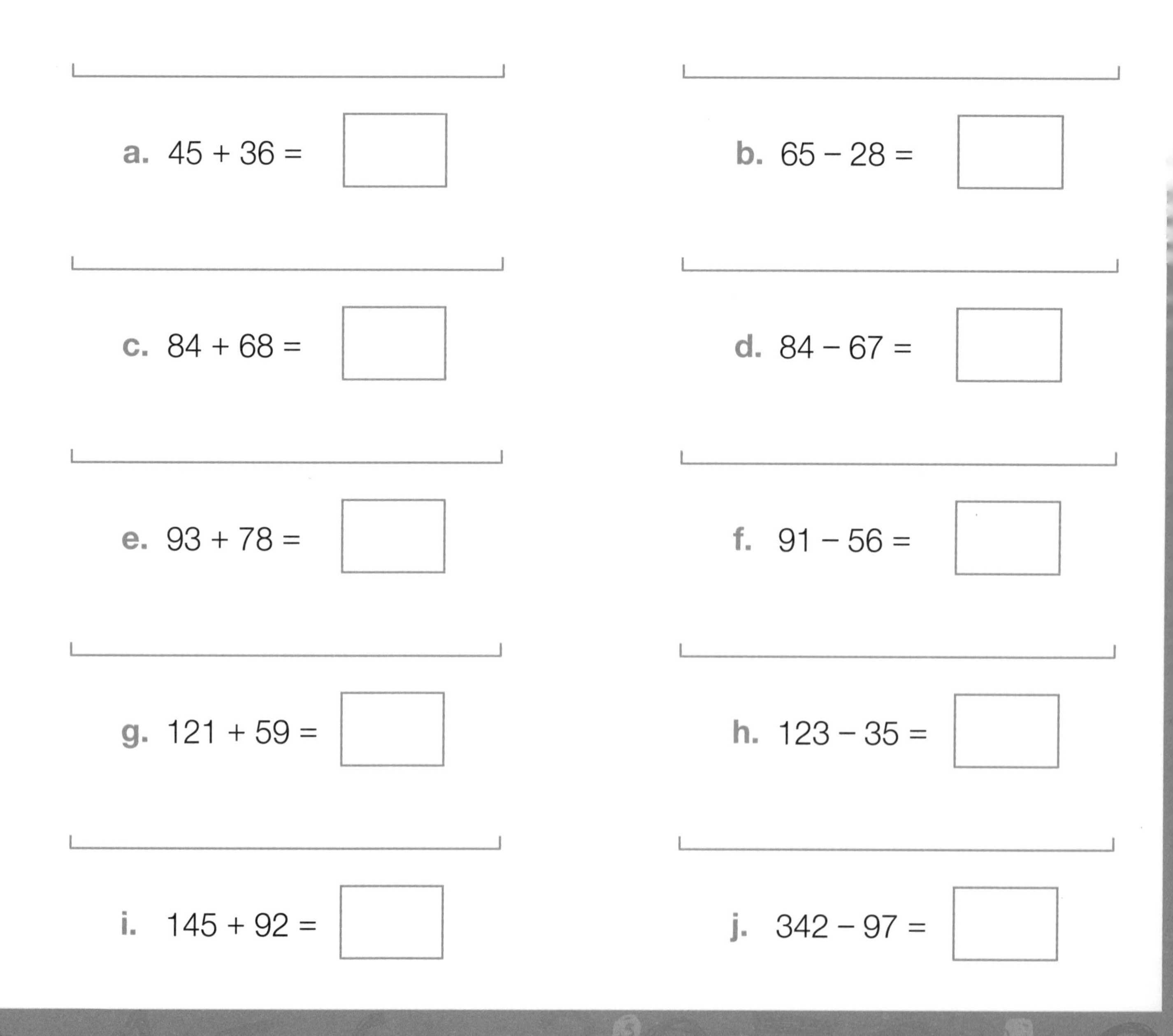

Estimating answers

Estimating answers helps to give us a rough idea of what the correct answer is before we work it out.

To estimate, look at the 10s numbers.

For **5**3 – **2**4, do **50** – **20** in your head. The estimated answer is 30. The actual answer is 29.

If the 1s number is 5 or more, round it up to the next 10 before estimating your answer. So for 5**8** – 24, do **60** – **20** = 40.

Here are some number sentences and some estimates of the answers.

1. For each, circle what you think is the best estimate then work out the answer.
2. Check your answers by adding the numbers in a different order.
3. Was your estimate a good one?

Number sentences	Estimates	True answer	Good or bad guess
53 + 28	60 70 80 90		
61 + 32	80 90 100 110		
96 – 31	50 60 70 80		
49 + 22	60 70 80 90		
95 – 48	40 50 60 70		

Sticker problems

Jamie likes to collect football stickers. Here are some problems about Jamie and his stickers.

1. Read the problems carefully. Write an addition or subtraction sentences for each problem and work out the answer. You will need to use the answer to the first problem to solve the next one, and so on.

a. Jamie used his pocket money to buy some stickers. He bought 15 English football stickers, double that number of Scottish stickers, and 20 Welsh ones. How many stickers did Jamie buy altogether? ☐	**b.** When Jamie got to school the next day he decided to give his best friend, Jon, half of his Scottish stickers. How many stickers did Jamie have left in total? ☐
c. On the way home from school Jamie decided to call in to see his cousin, Ellie. Ellie also collects stickers and she has a total of 47 stickers. They looked at their stickers together. Jamie gave Ellie 10 of his stickers. How many stickers does Jamie have now? ☐ How many stickers does Ellie have now? ☐	**d.** Jamie's dad gave Jamie another 30 stickers. However, Jamie already had 13 of these so he decided to give the 13 to his friend Jon. How many stickers does Jamie have now? ☐

Column addition

Here is 342 + 89 on a number line.

+80 +9

342 422 431

Here is the same sum using column addition:

	3 4 2	
+	8 9	
	1 1	Add the 1s
	1 2 0	Add the 10s
	3 0 0	Add the 100s
	4 3 1	Work out the total

1. Work out the answers to each of these questions using two different methods. Use a horizontal method first. Then use the column addition method. Write the answer. Check that both methods give the same answer.

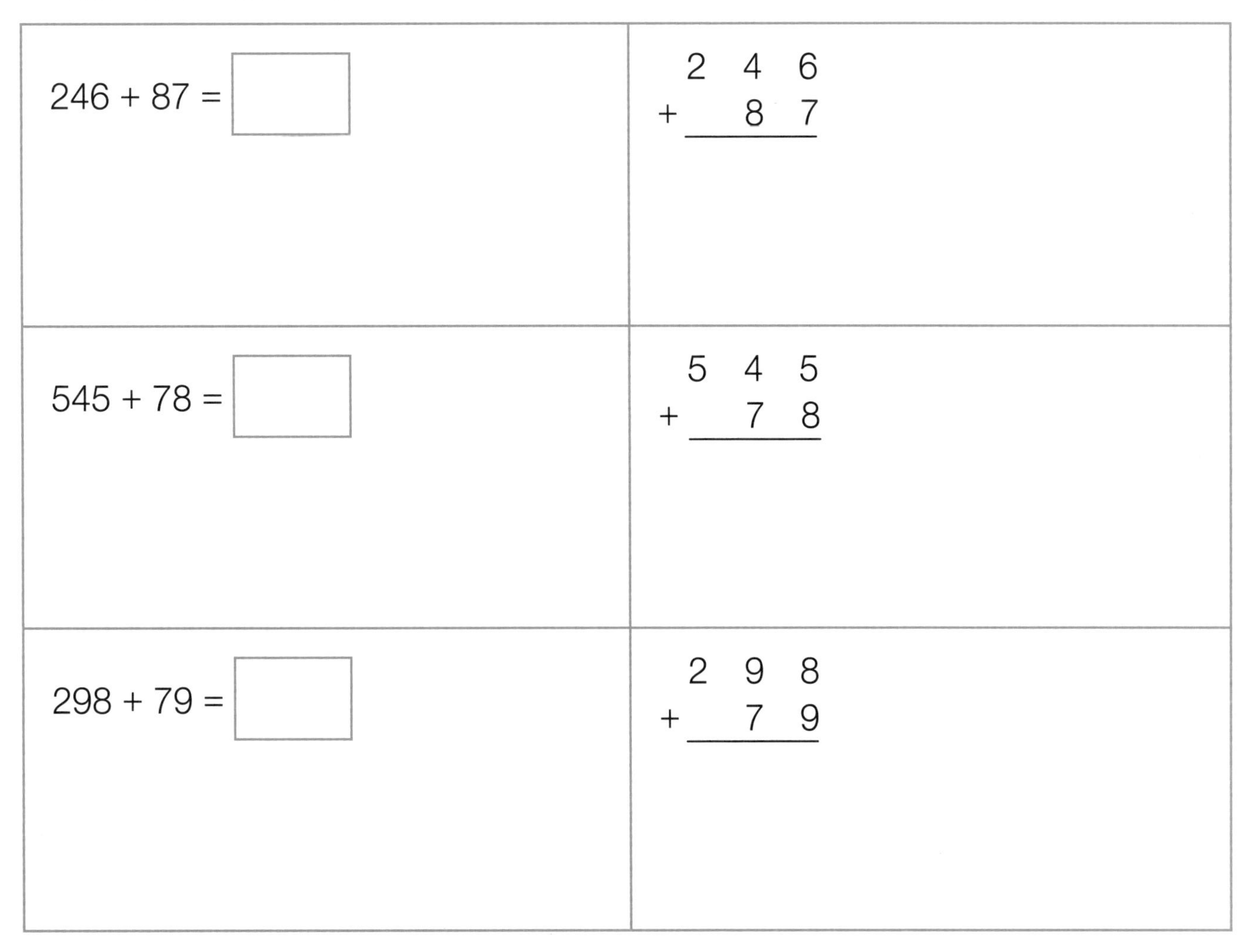

246 + 87 = ☐	2 4 6 + 8 7
545 + 78 = ☐	5 4 5 + 7 8
298 + 79 = ☐	2 9 8 + 7 9

Column subtraction

To use column subtraction for pairs of numbers, you can partition each number to make it easier.

	8	7	4	→	800	and	70	and	4	
−	2	6	3	−	200	and	60	and	3	
	6	1	1		600	and	10	and	1	= 611

1. Partition the numbers to help you subtract.

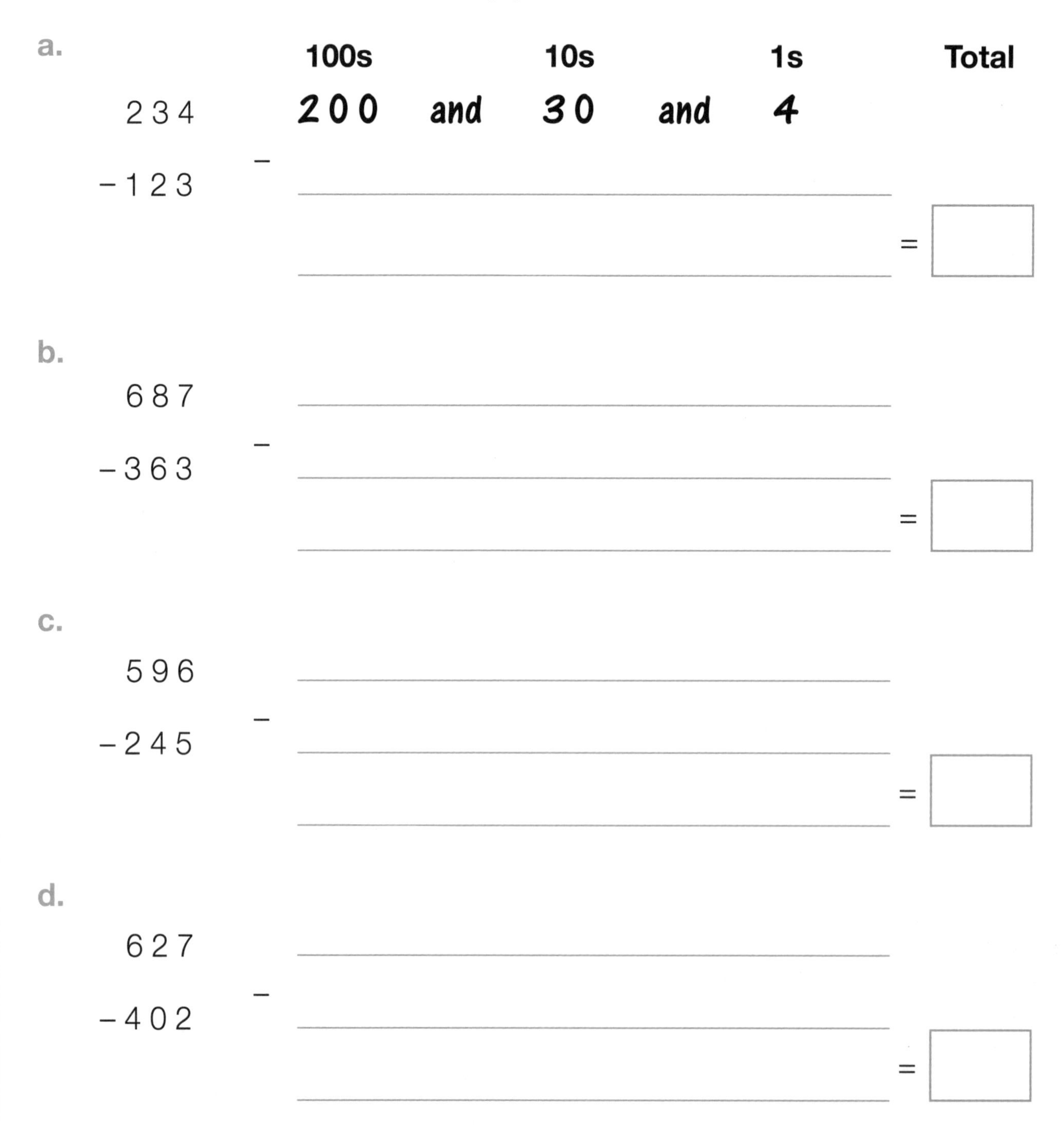

a.

	100s		10s		1s	Total
234	200	and	30	and	4	
−123						
						= ☐

b.

687

−363

= ☐

c.

596

−245

= ☐

d.

627

−402

= ☐

You can also change 10s or 100s in subtraction.

$^{3}\not{4}$ $^{1}\,^{4}\not{5}$ $^{1}2$	Subtract the 1s: you can't subtract 5 from 2, so change
− 2 7 5	a 10 (12 − 5).
7	Subtract the 10s: you can't subtract 7 from 4, so change
7 0	a 100 (14 − 7).
1 0 0	Subtract the 100s: (3 − 2).
1 7 7	Find the total.

When you are confident with the above steps, try doing them in your head.

1. Use columns to help you work out these subtractions. You may need to change 10s or 100s to subtract these numbers.

4 5 3 −2 4 6 Subtract 1s Subtract 10s ______ Subtract 100s ______ Work out the total.	7 3 2 −3 5 8 Subtract 1s Subtract 10s ______ Subtract 100s ______ Work out the total.
6 2 4 −4 7 5 Subtract 1s Subtract 10s ______ Subtract 100s ______ Work out the total.	9 4 1 −5 6 7 Subtract 1s Subtract 10s ______ Subtract 100s ______ Work out the total.

2. Now try subtracting the 1s, 10s and 100s in your head.

4 7 2 −1 4 6 ______	6 2 4 −3 7 6 ______
5 8 1 − 9 6 ______	8 5 3 −4 9 7 ______

Multiples of 3 and 4

Venn diagrams help you to sort information under two different headings. Items in the middle section will match both headings.

1. Write all the multiples of 3 that are less than 40 in a list. Now sort them on the diagram.

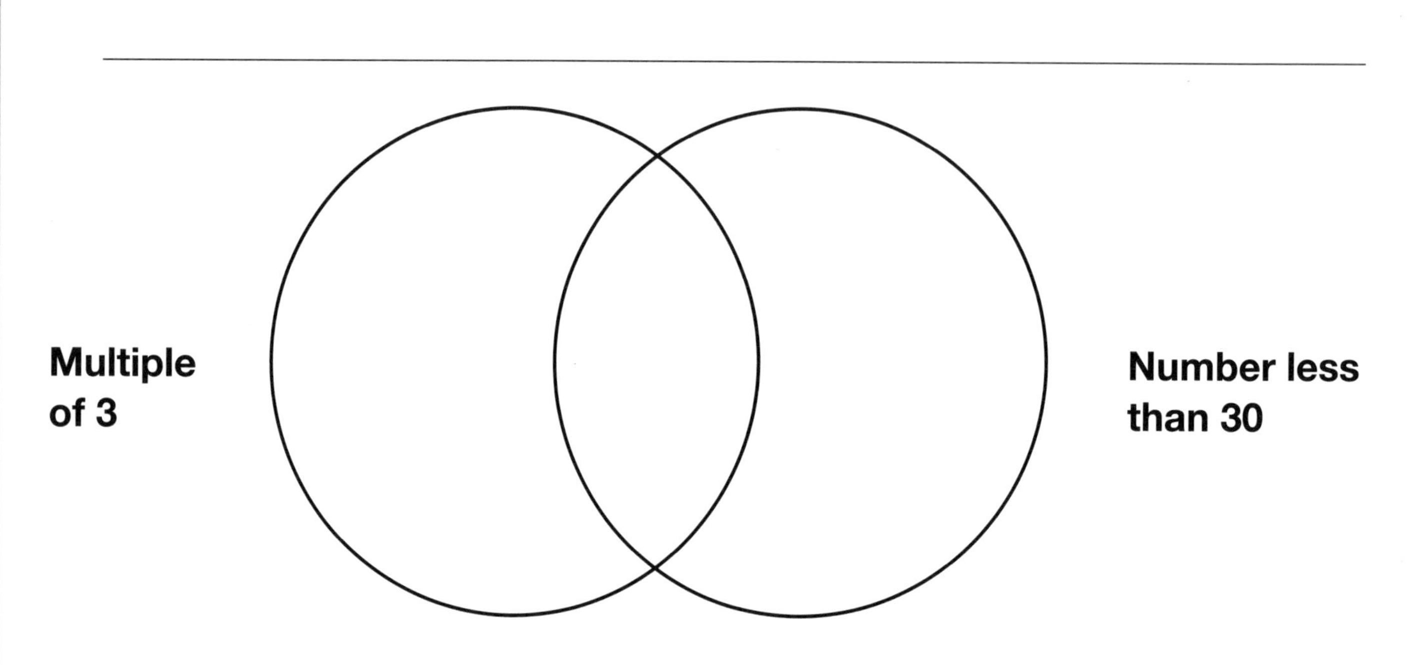

2. Write all the multiples of 4 that are less than 50 in a list. Sort these on the diagram below.

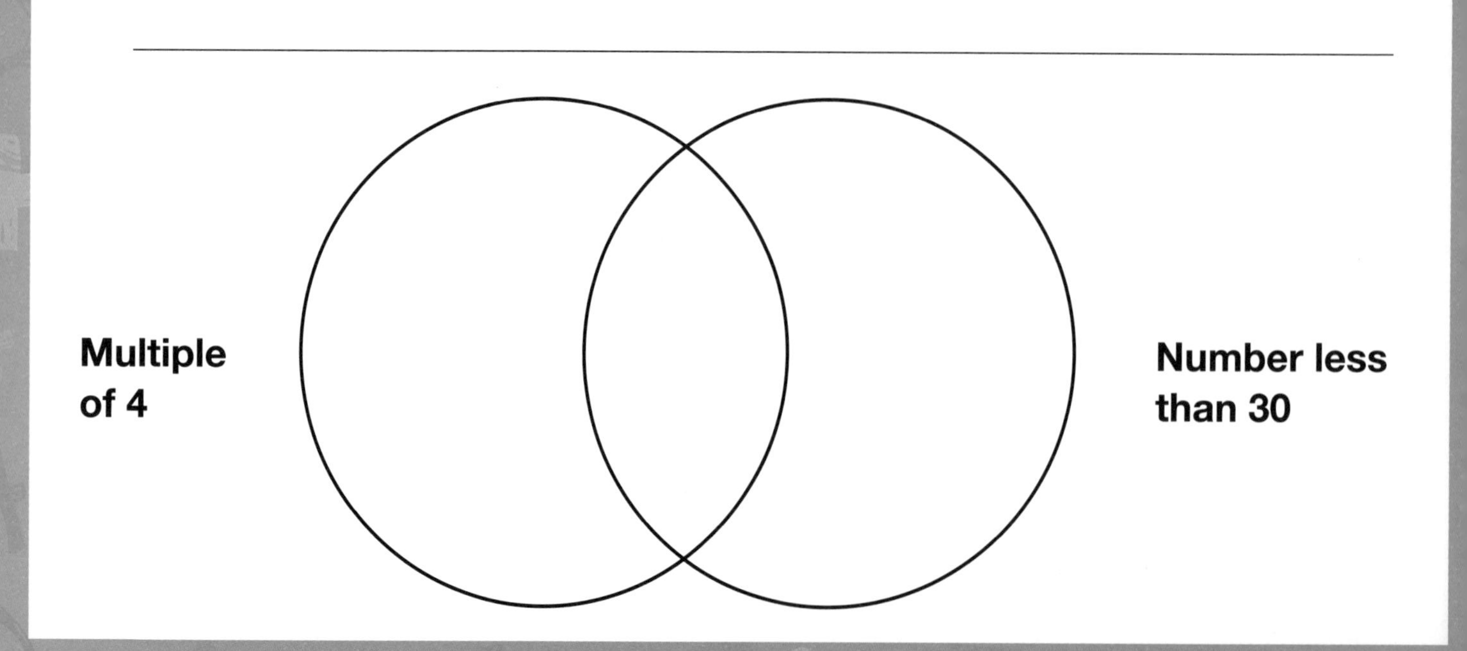

Carroll diagrams offer another way of grouping things into different categories.

4. Write the numbers 1 to 40 in this Carroll diagram.

	Multiple of 4	Not a multiple of 4
Multiple of 3		
Not a multiple of 3		

The 8-times table

Practise saying the 8-times table. You may want to write it down to help you.

Multiples of 8 are all even numbers. If you know $4 \times 8 = 32$ you also know that $32 \div 8 = 4$.

1. Answer the questions below.

1 spider = 8 legs

a. 6 spiders = how many legs? ☐

b. 9 spiders = how many legs? ☐

c. 4 spiders = how many legs? ☐

d. 3 spiders = how many legs? ☐

e. 8 spiders = how many legs? ☐

f. 2 spiders = how many legs? ☐

g. 10 spiders = how many legs? ☐

2. Draw a line to the correct answer.

48 legs = how many spiders?		4 spiders
64 legs = how many spiders?		2 spiders
32 legs = how many spiders?		10 spiders
80 legs = how many spiders?		8 spiders
16 legs = how many spiders?		6 spiders

3. Complete the sentence.

Multiples of 8 are always ____________________ numbers.

Relationship between × and ÷

Knowing multiplication facts helps us work out related division facts.

For example, $3 \times 8 = 24$ so $24 \div 8 = 3$.

1. Fill in the missing words or digits.

a. Eighty ÷ ten = ______________

______________ × ten = eighty

b. 27 ÷ ______ = 9

9 × ______ = 27

c. ______ ÷ 4 = 7

7 × ______ = 28

d. ______________ ÷ four = eight

Eight × four = ______________

2. Fill in the blanks.

a. You know 21 ÷ 3 = ______ so 7 × 3 = ______ and 3 × 7 = ______

b. You know 16 ÷ 2 = ______ so 8 × 2 = ______ and 16 ÷ 8 = ______

c. You know 10 × 6 = ______ so 60 ÷ 6 = ______ and 60 ÷ 10 = ______

3. Write four facts using the digits 7, 5 and 35.

______ × ______ = ______ ______ ÷ ______ = ______

______ × ______ = ______ ______ ÷ ______ = ______

Multiply using teen numbers

Practise saying the 2-, 3-, 4-, 5-, 8- and 10-times tables.

To multiply by a 'teen' number, partition the number.

For example, 4 × 16, work out 4 × 10 (**40**) and 4 × 6 (**24**) and then add them: **40** + **24** = 64.

Complete the table.

1. Choose a number from the grid.
2. Choose a number from the row.
3. Multiply your grid number by your row number.
4. Do this five times using a different pair of numbers each time.

Grid numbers

11	16	19	12	14
15	18	10	13	17

Row numbers

2 3 4 5 6 10

Grid number	Row number	Number sentence	Jottings	Answer

Tens and units multiplication

To multiply a 2-digit number by a 1-digit number, first partition the 2-digit number into 10s and 1s.

For example, for 32 × 2, partition 32 into 30 and 2.

$30 \times 2 = 60$
$2 \times 2 = \underline{\ \ 4}$
$60 + 4 = \underline{64}$

1. Now try this method for these multiplication sentences.

a. 43 × 2	b. 23 × 2
c. 24 × 3	d. 48 × 2
e. 14 × 3	f. 26 × 4

Short multiplication

We can use columns to work out multiplication. This will help when we need to multiply larger numbers.

For example, 34 × 4:

$$\begin{array}{r} 3\ 4 \\ \times \quad 4 \\ \hline 1\ 3\ 6 \\ \hline {\scriptstyle 1}\ \ \end{array}$$

Multiply the 1s: (4 × 4 = 16)

Write the 6 in the 1s column and write the 1 below the line, in the 10s column.

Multiply the 10s: (3 × 4 = 12, then add the 1 that was carried over = 13).

Write this answer in the 100s and 10s columns.

1. Answer these questions. Remember to multiply the 1s, then multiply the 10s.

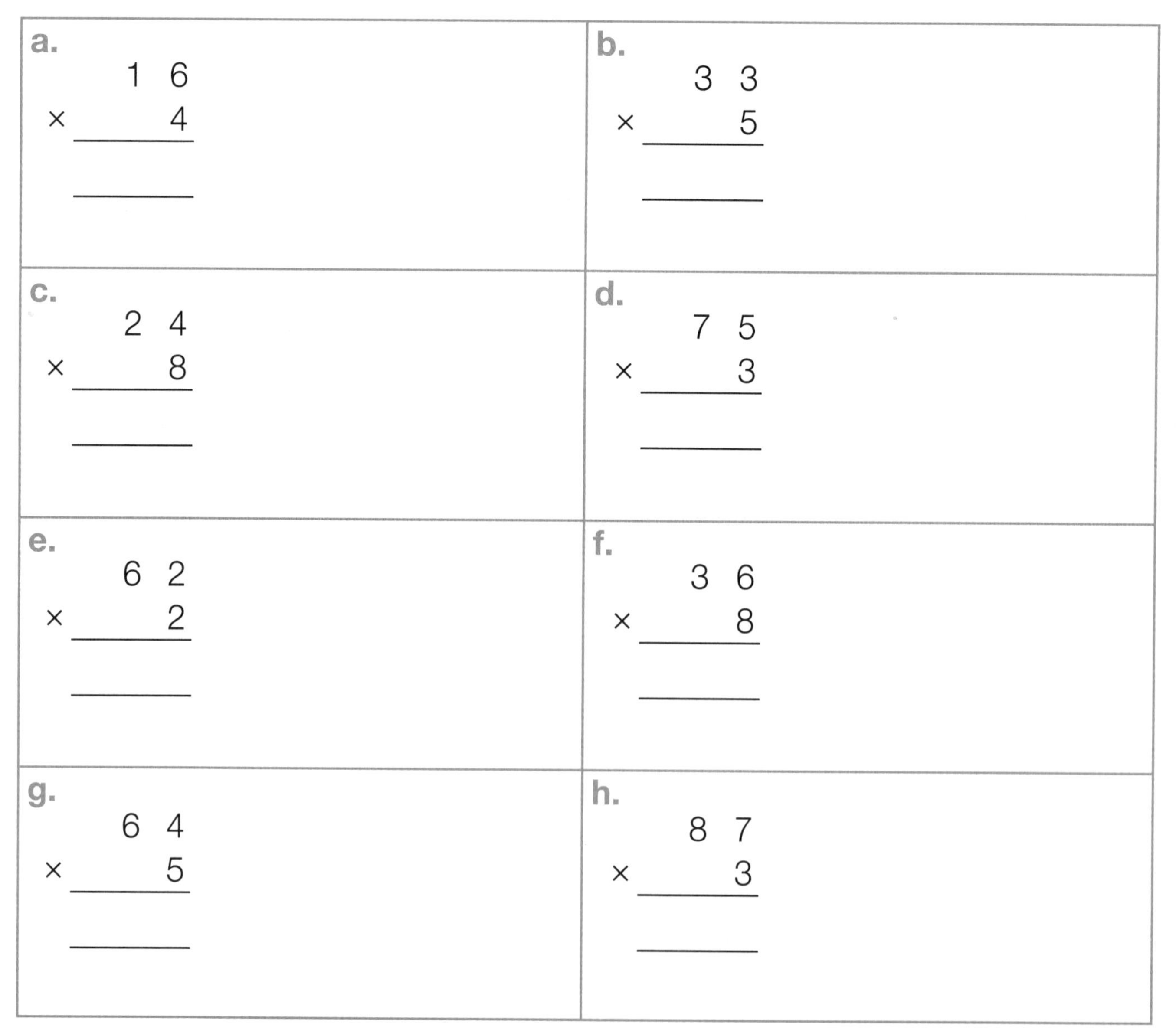

a. 16 × 4 = ____	**b.** 33 × 5 = ____
c. 24 × 8 = ____	**d.** 75 × 3 = ____
e. 62 × 2 = ____	**f.** 36 × 8 = ____
g. 64 × 5 = ____	**h.** 87 × 3 = ____

Division hops

This number line helps us solve the division question 15 ÷ 5.
There are 5 jumps of 3, so 15 ÷ 5 = 3.

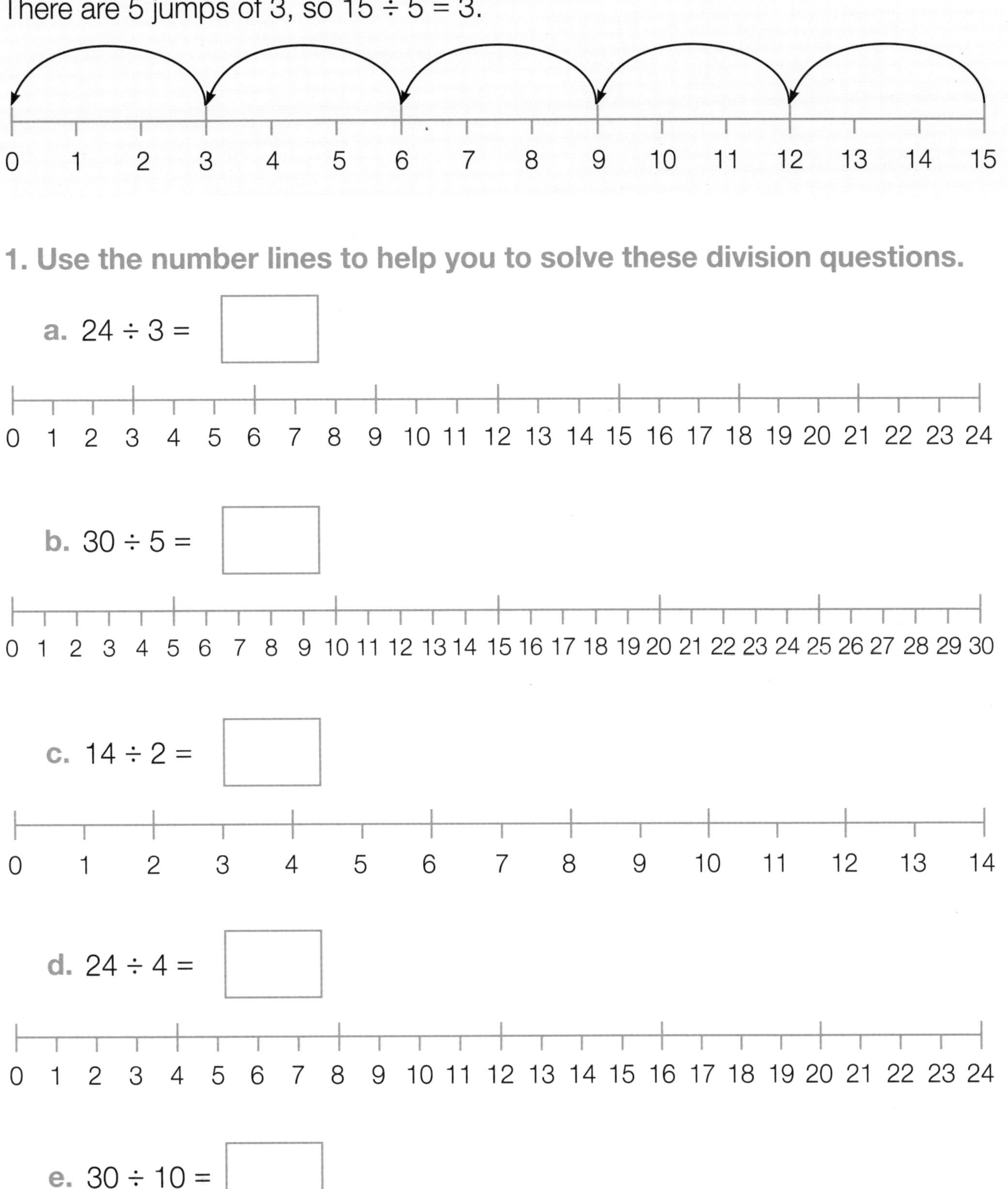

1. Use the number lines to help you to solve these division questions.

a. 24 ÷ 3 = ☐

0 1 2 3 4 5 6 7 8 9 10 11 12 13 14 15 16 17 18 19 20 21 22 23 24

b. 30 ÷ 5 = ☐

0 1 2 3 4 5 6 7 8 9 10 11 12 13 14 15 16 17 18 19 20 21 22 23 24 25 26 27 28 29 30

c. 14 ÷ 2 = ☐

0 1 2 3 4 5 6 7 8 9 10 11 12 13 14

d. 24 ÷ 4 = ☐

0 1 2 3 4 5 6 7 8 9 10 11 12 13 14 15 16 17 18 19 20 21 22 23 24

e. 30 ÷ 10 = ☐

0 1 2 3 4 5 6 7 8 9 10 11 12 13 14 15 16 17 18 19 20 21 22 23 24 25 26 27 28 29 30

Division facts

Practise saying the 2-, 3-, 4-, 5-, 8- and 10-times tables.

Ask yourself: *How many 3s are there in 24?*

Count in 3s on your fingers to find out: 24 ÷ 3 = 8.

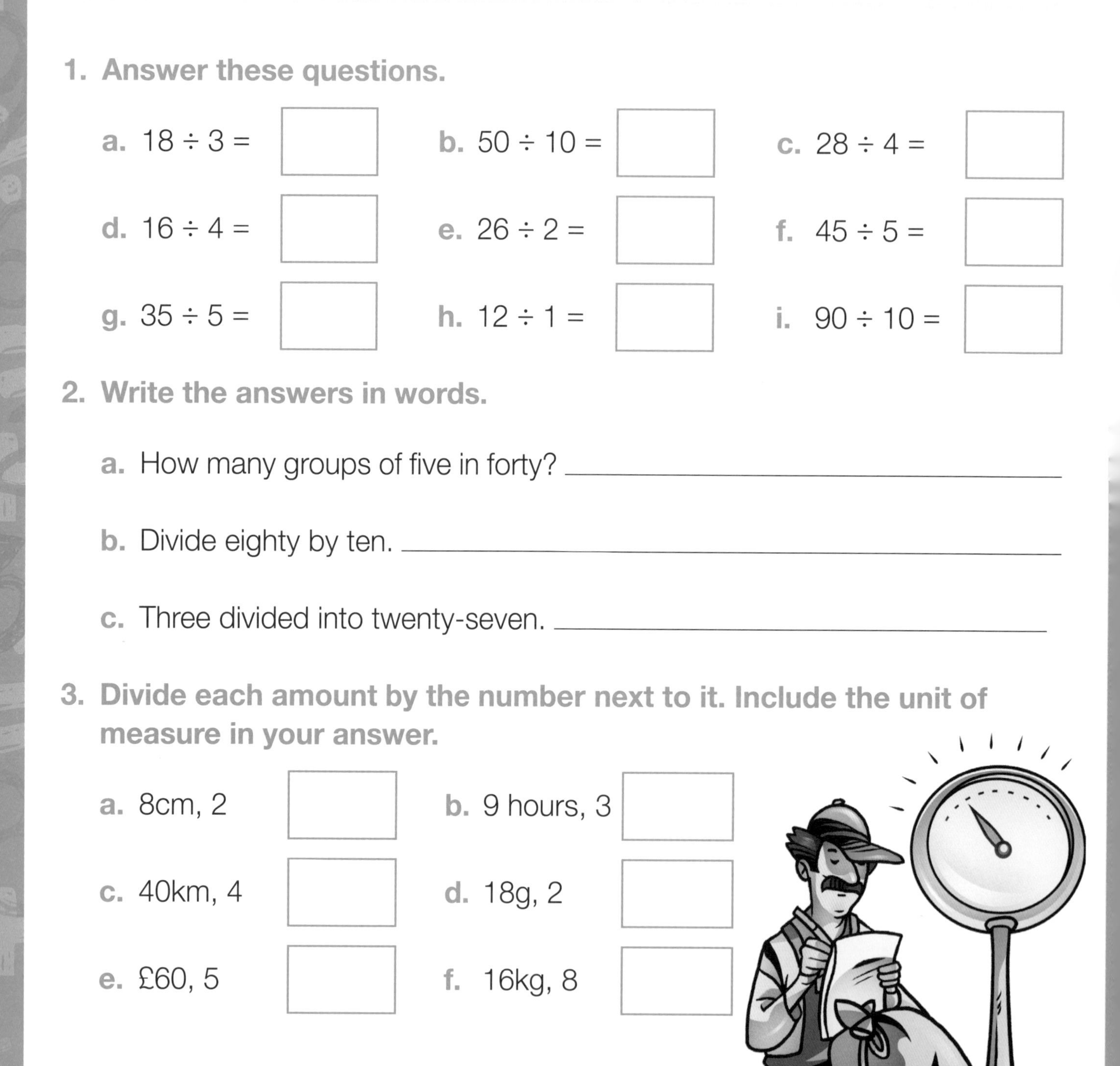

1. Answer these questions.

a. 18 ÷ 3 = ☐ b. 50 ÷ 10 = ☐ c. 28 ÷ 4 = ☐

d. 16 ÷ 4 = ☐ e. 26 ÷ 2 = ☐ f. 45 ÷ 5 = ☐

g. 35 ÷ 5 = ☐ h. 12 ÷ 1 = ☐ i. 90 ÷ 10 = ☐

2. Write the answers in words.

a. How many groups of five in forty? ____________________

b. Divide eighty by ten. ____________________

c. Three divided into twenty-seven. ____________________

3. Divide each amount by the number next to it. Include the unit of measure in your answer.

a. 8cm, 2 ☐ b. 9 hours, 3 ☐

c. 40km, 4 ☐ d. 18g, 2 ☐

e. £60, 5 ☐ f. 16kg, 8 ☐

Short division

We can use written or short division to help us divide larger numbers.

For example, 96 ÷ 4 becomes:

```
    2  4
4 | 9 ¹6
```

Answer = 24

First divide the 10s: 9 ÷ 4 = 2.
Write 2 in the 10s column and write the left-over 1 in the 1s column.
Then divide the 1s: 16 ÷ 4 = 4.
Write 4 in the 1s column.

1. Work out the 10s first, followed by the 1s.

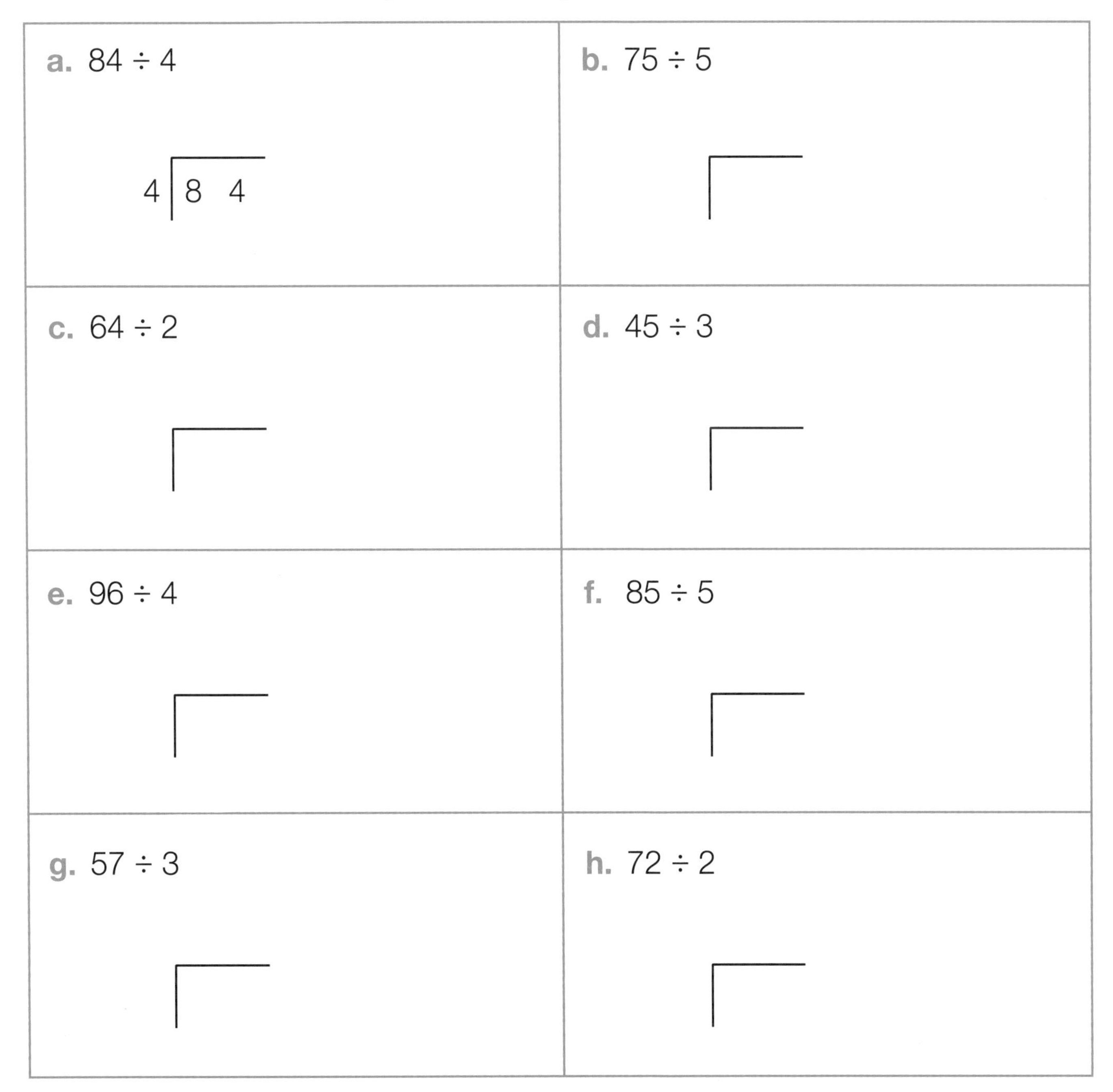

a. 84 ÷ 4

4 | 8 4

b. 75 ÷ 5

c. 64 ÷ 2

d. 45 ÷ 3

e. 96 ÷ 4

f. 85 ÷ 5

g. 57 ÷ 3

h. 72 ÷ 2

Multiplication and division word problems

1. Read each problem and ask yourself:
   Is this a multiplication or division question?
   Write a multiplication or division sentence for the problem, then work out the answer.
   Write down your method.

Word problem	Method	Answer
There are 60 children in Year 3 at Downford Primary School. Their teachers decide to put them into groups of five. How many groups is that?		
There are three classes in Year 1. Each class has 35 pairs of scissors. How many pairs of scissors is that in total?		
The children in Class 2 ate 75 school meals in one school week. How many children ate school dinners?		
There are 64 children who eat sandwiches for lunch. How many sandwich lunches is that in one week?		

2. **Read each problem. Ask yourself:** ***Is it a one- or two-step problem? Is this a written multiplication or division problem?*** **Write down your method.**

Word problem	Method	Answer
There are five boxes of cakes. Each box has 14 cakes in it. How many cakes is that altogether?		
The baker made 12 chocolate cakes and 14 vanilla cakes. The cakes are packed into boxes of six. How many boxes can be filled?		
There are 64 chocolate flakes on the shelf. Half of these are sold. Half of what is left are put into a tray. How many are left now?		
The baker makes 25 white loaves and 20 brown ones. The loaves are packed into cartons that hold six loaves each. How many cartons are needed?		

Fraction search

A fraction is an equal part of a number, an amount or a shape.

$\frac{3}{4}$

3 ← The top number (or numerator) tells us the number of parts of the whole.

4 ← The bottom number (or denominator) tells us the number of parts the whole is divided into.

1. Draw a line to join each picture to its corresponding fraction.

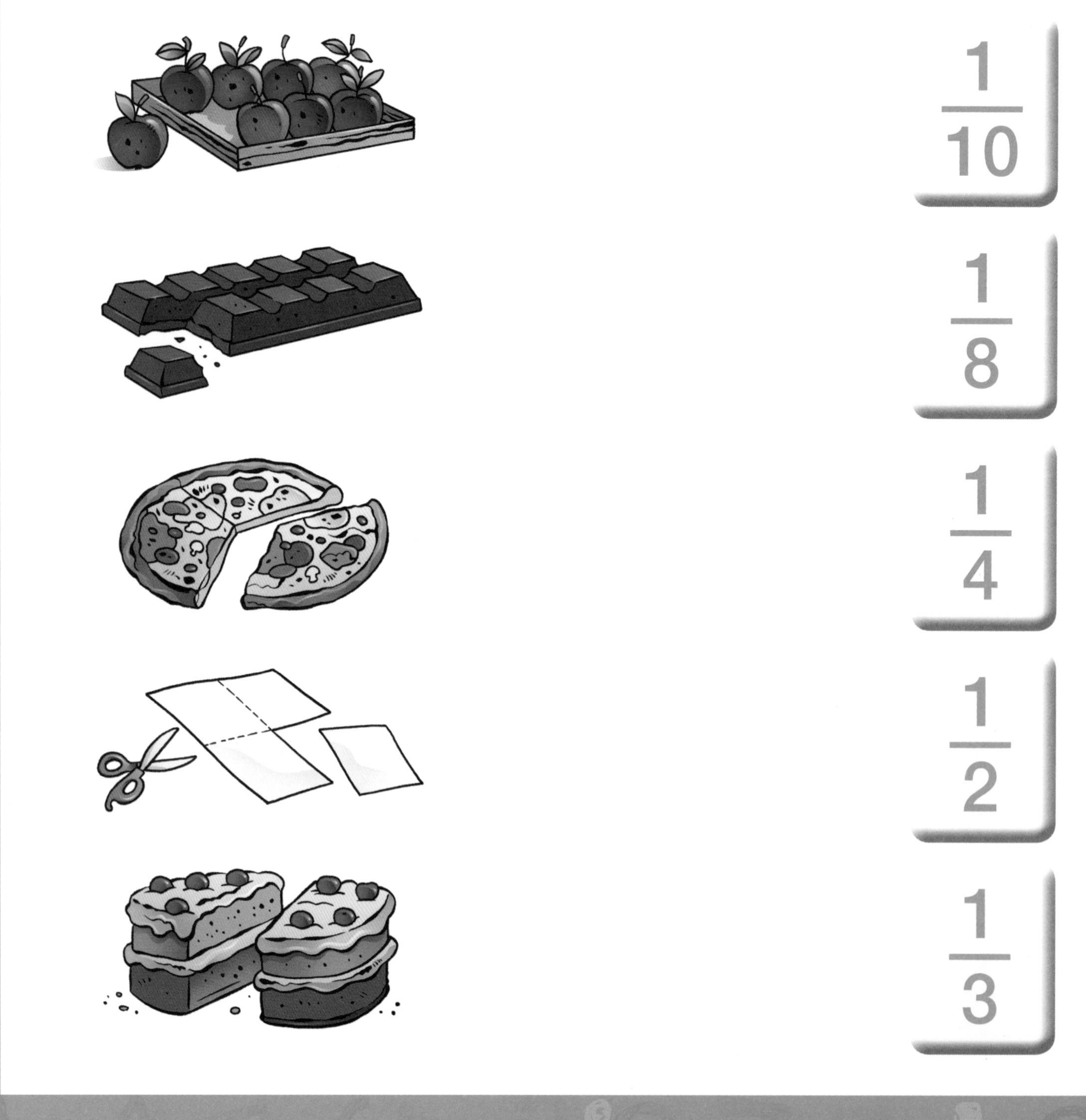

Non-unit fractions

A non-unit fraction is a fraction where the numerator (the top number) is not 1.
So $\frac{2}{5}$, $\frac{3}{4}$ and $\frac{5}{6}$ are all non-unit fractions.
To find $\frac{2}{5}$ of 20, first find $\frac{1}{5}$ of 20. 20 ÷ 5 = 4, then times by 2, so: $\frac{2}{5} = 2 \times 4 = 8$.

1. For each shape, colour the number of parts shown by the fraction.

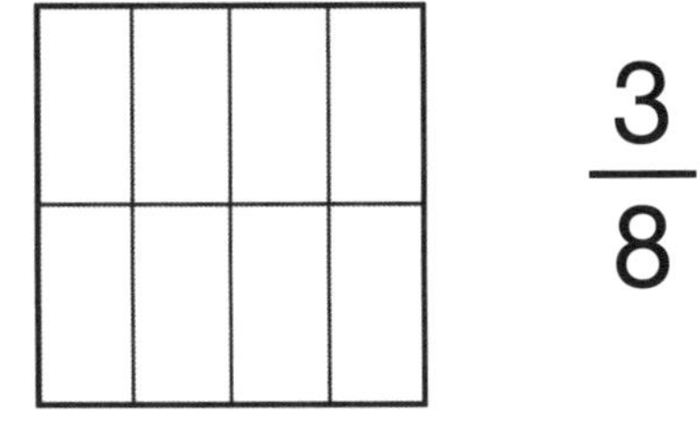

$\frac{3}{8}$

$\frac{2}{3}$

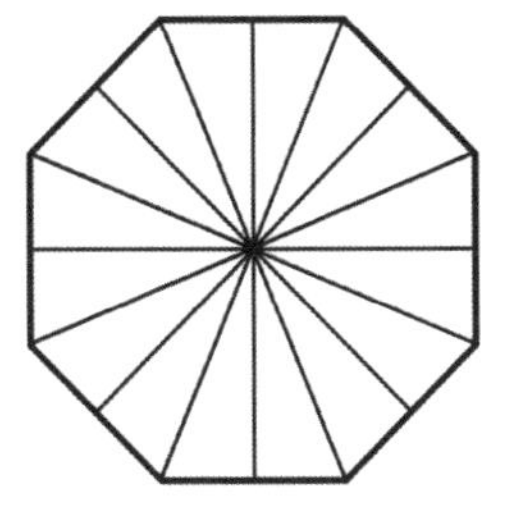

$\frac{3}{4}$

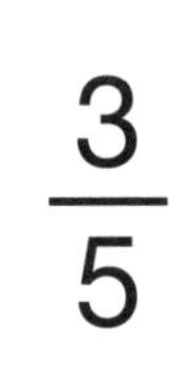

$\frac{3}{5}$

2. Draw a ring round the number of things shown by each fraction.

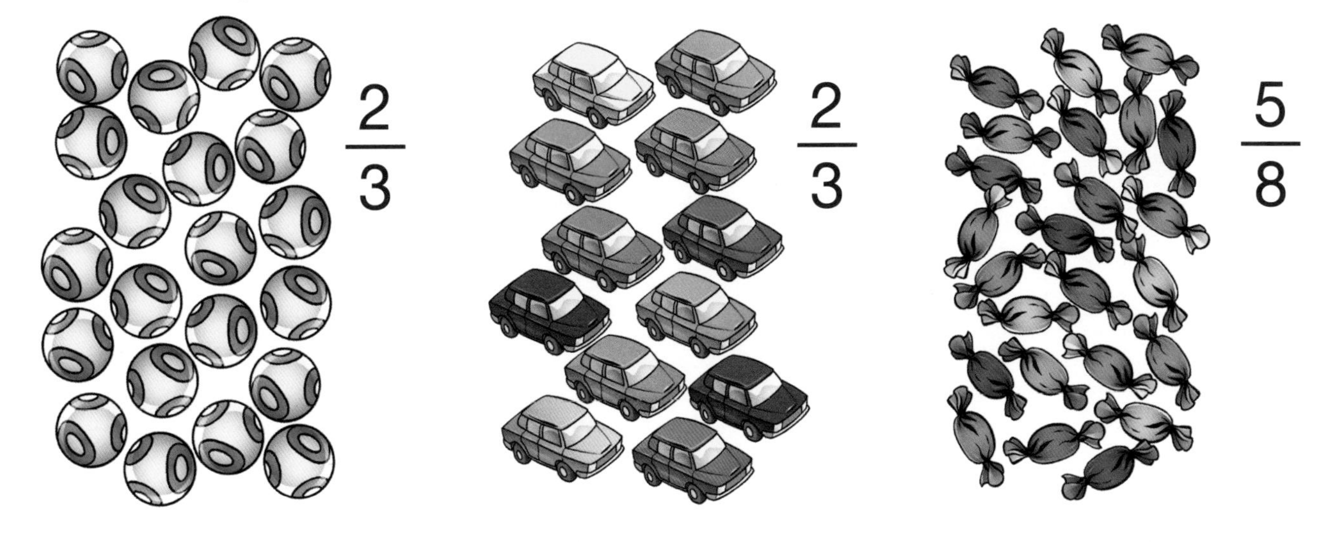

$\frac{2}{3}$ $\frac{2}{3}$ $\frac{5}{8}$

3. Answer these questions.

a. What is $\frac{3}{4}$ of 100cm? ☐

b. What is $\frac{3}{5}$ of 400g? ☐

c. What is $\frac{2}{3}$ of 150ml? ☐

Equivalent fractions: numbers

An equivalent fraction is a fraction which is the same as another fraction, but looks different.

To work out if fractions are equivalent, divide the top and bottom number by the same number.

For example, with $\frac{4}{20}$ you can divide the top and bottom number by 4.

$4 \div 4 = 1$ and $20 \div 4 = 5$. So $\frac{4}{20}$ is the same as $\frac{1}{5}$. They are equivalent fractions.

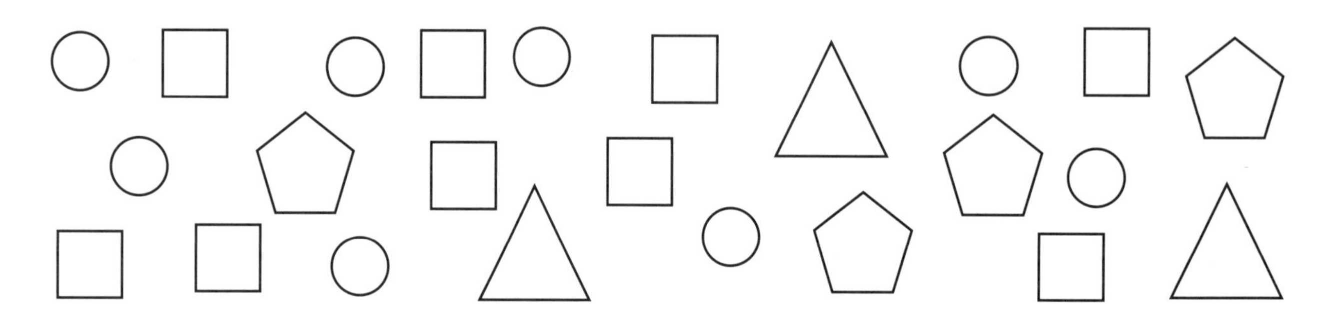

1. Look at the shapes above. Write down what fraction of the total they are. The first one has been done for you.

Shape	Simple fraction	Equivalent fraction
Triangles	$\frac{3}{24}$	$\frac{1}{8}$
Squares		
Circles		
Pentagons		
Triangles and squares		

2. Complete these equivalent fractions:

$\frac{1}{2} = \frac{\square}{6} = \frac{12}{\square} = \frac{\square}{10}$

$\frac{1}{4} = \frac{\square}{8} = \frac{5}{\square} = \frac{\square}{16}$

Equivalent fractions: shapes

Count the total number of parts to find the denominator.

Count the number of shaded parts to find the numerator. This gives you the simple fraction, such as $\frac{3}{9}$.

To find an equivalent, divide or multiply the top and bottom by the same number. For example, $\frac{3}{9} = \frac{1}{3} = \frac{5}{15}$.

1. **Look carefully at each shape. Decide what fraction has been shaded.**
2. **Now write two fractions for the shaded part. The first one has been done for you.**

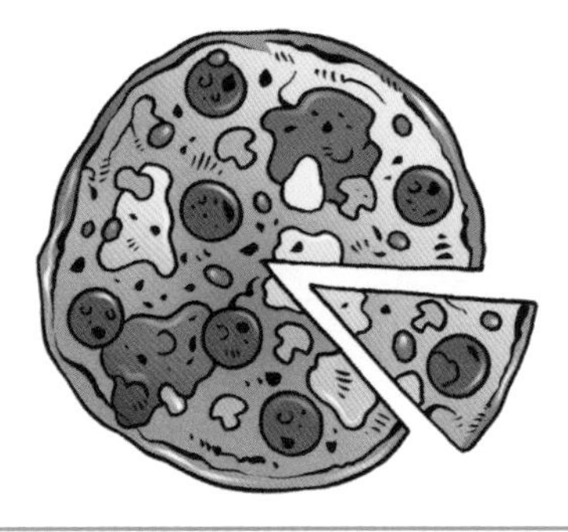

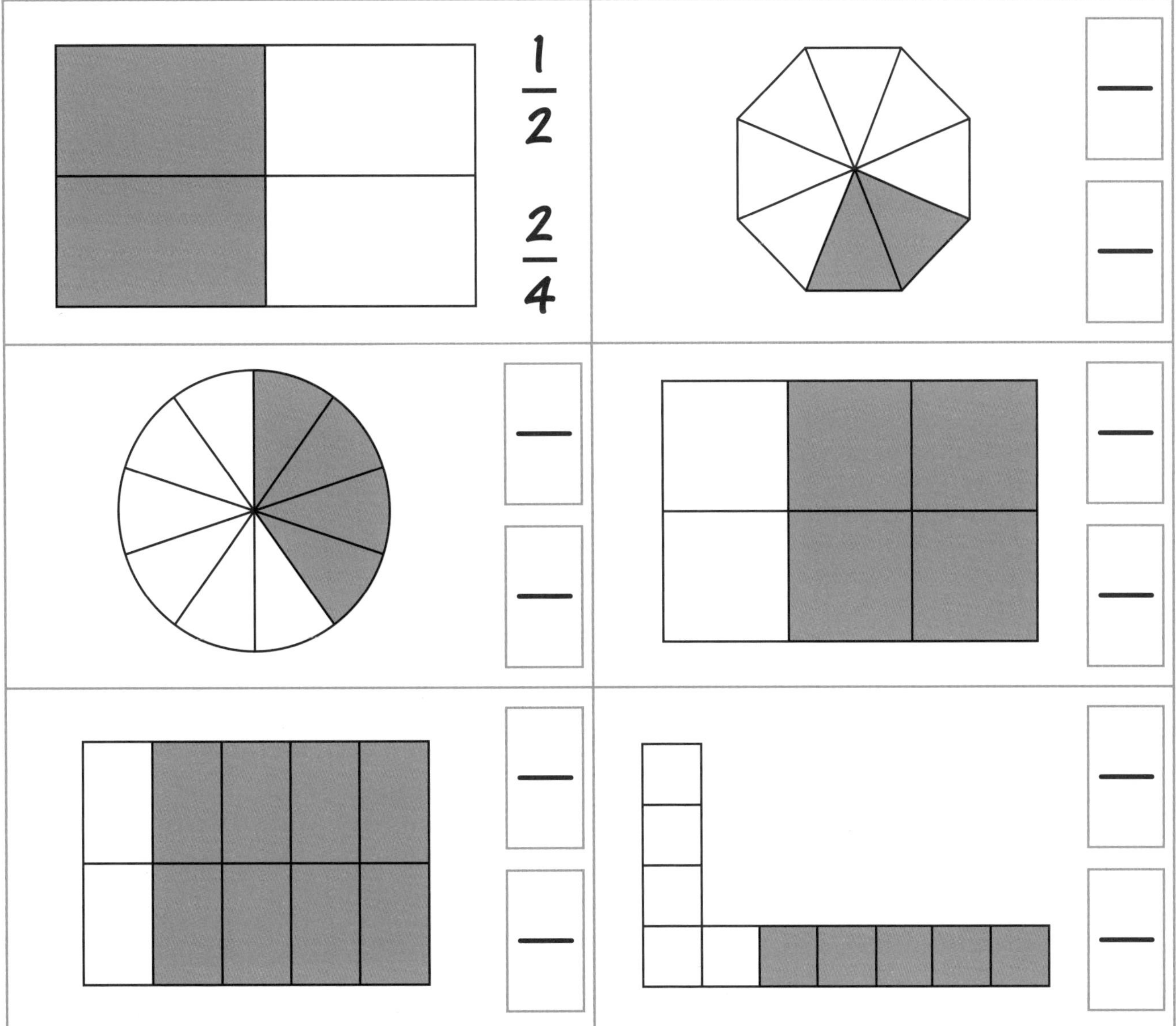

Ordering fractions

To order fractions with different denominators, you should first make all the denominators the same, for example:

To order these fractions: $\frac{1}{5}, \frac{3}{5}, \frac{3}{10}$, first make all the fractions into tenths by writing the equivalent fractions:

$(\frac{1}{5})\ \frac{2}{10}, (\frac{3}{5})\ \frac{6}{10}, \frac{3}{10}$

The fractions can now easily be put into order: $\frac{1}{5}, \frac{3}{10}, \frac{3}{5}$

1. Decide where these fractions will fit on each number line.

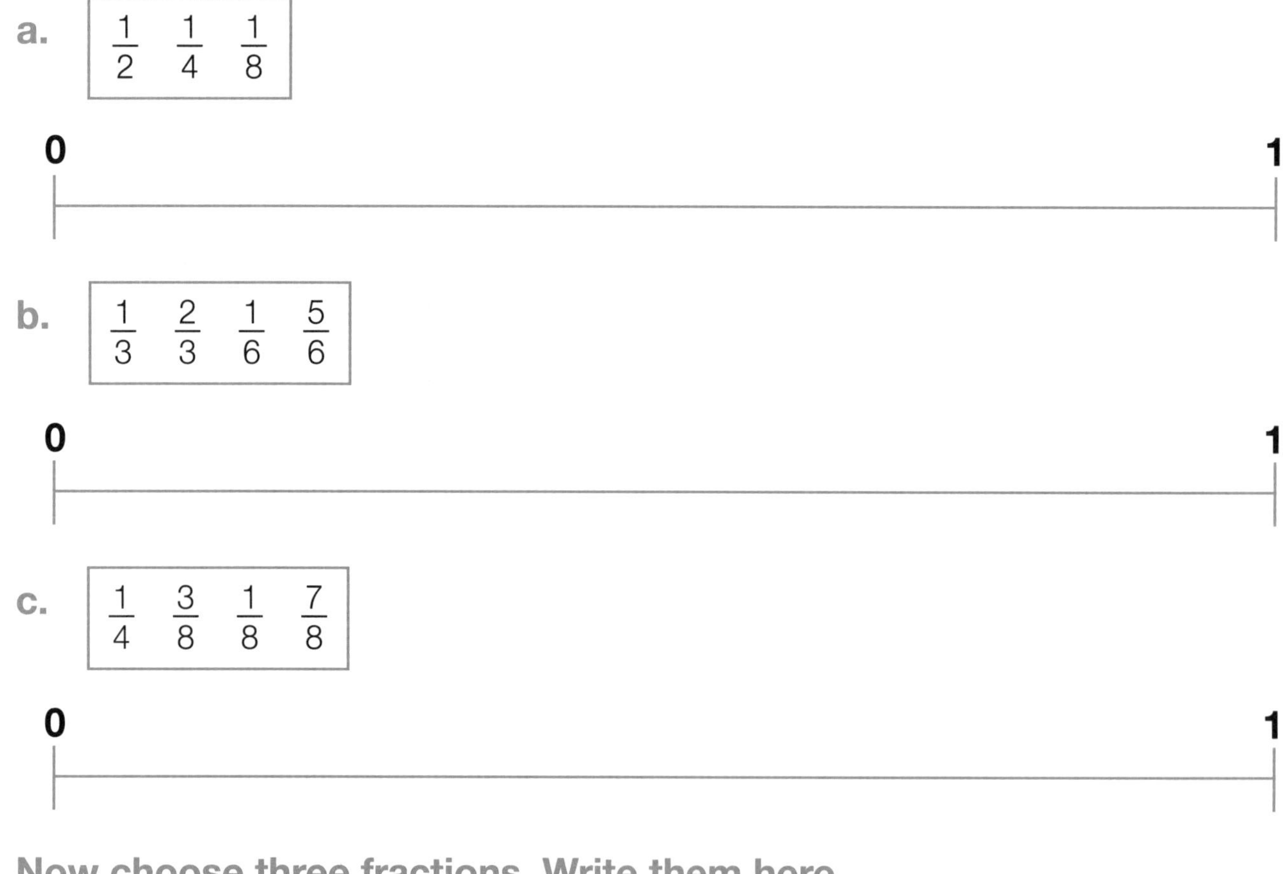

2. Now choose three fractions. Write them here.

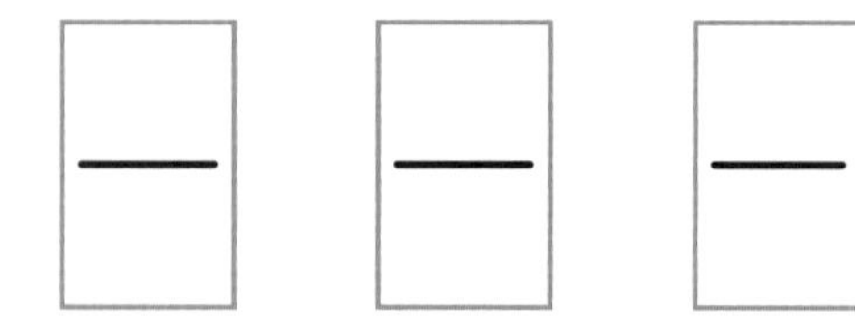

3. Write the three fractions on this number line.

0 1

Adding and subtracting fractions

To add or subtract fractions with the same denominator (the bottom number), simply add or subtract the numerators (the top number).

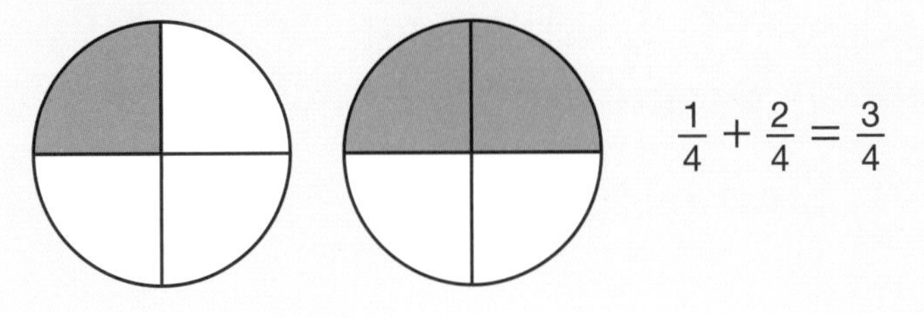

$\frac{1}{4} + \frac{2}{4} = \frac{3}{4}$

1. Count the shaded parts to help you add these fractions.

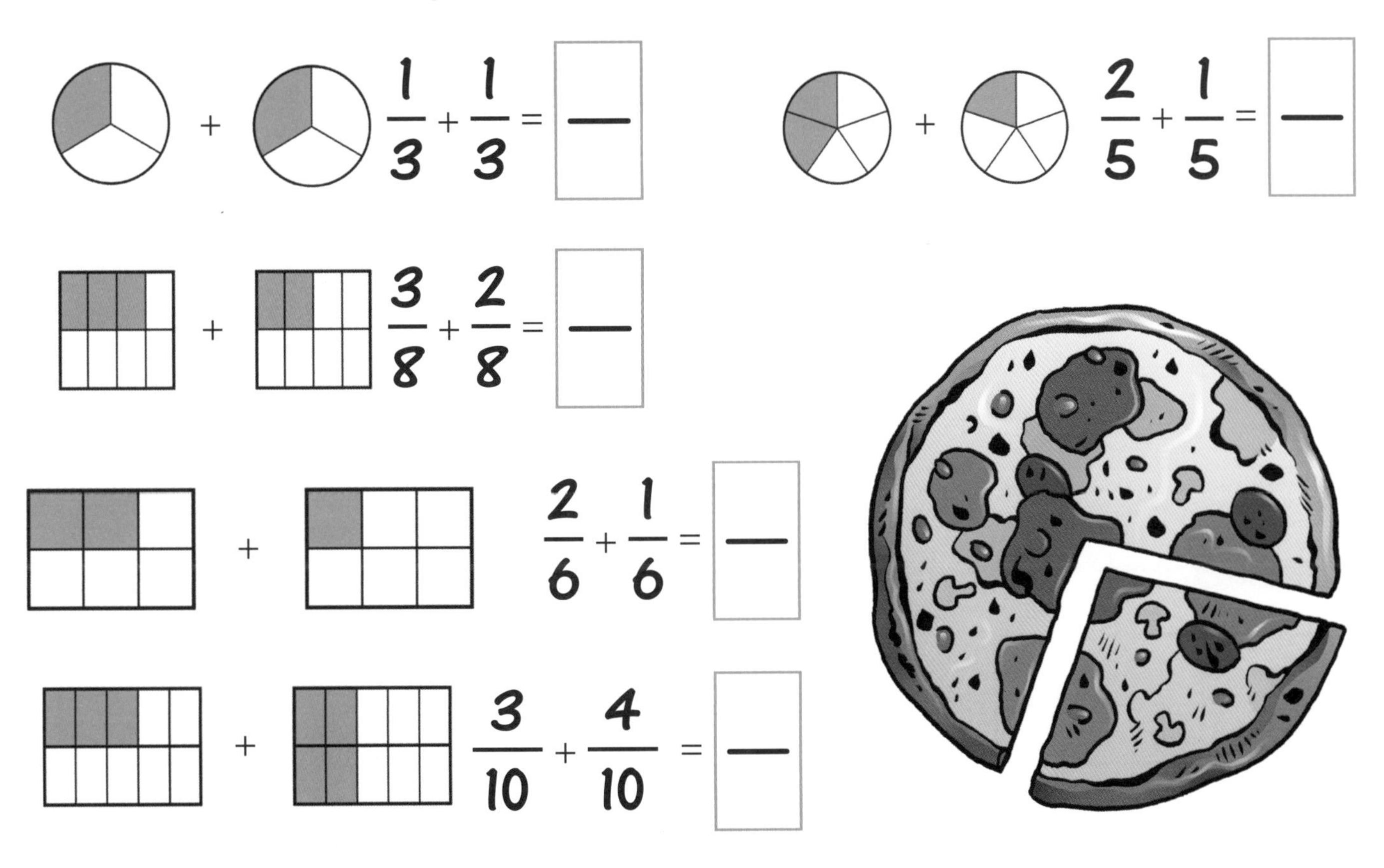

$\frac{1}{3} + \frac{1}{3} = \frac{\square}{\square}$

$\frac{2}{5} + \frac{1}{5} = \frac{\square}{\square}$

$\frac{3}{8} + \frac{2}{8} = \frac{\square}{\square}$

$\frac{2}{6} + \frac{1}{6} = \frac{\square}{\square}$

$\frac{3}{10} + \frac{4}{10} = \frac{\square}{\square}$

2. Now subtract the shaded part of these shapes.

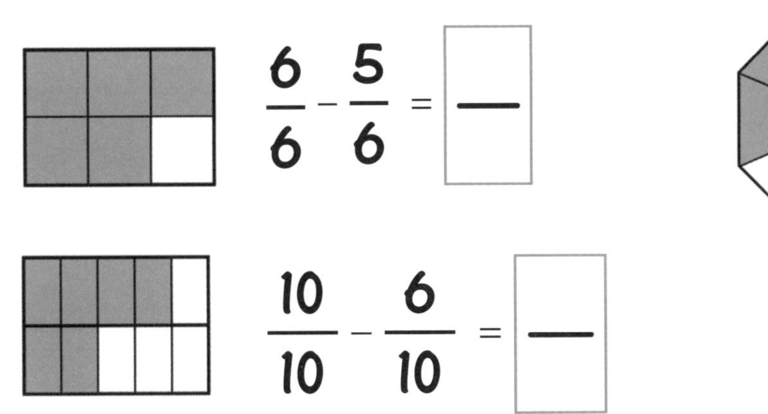

$\frac{6}{6} - \frac{5}{6} = \frac{\square}{\square}$

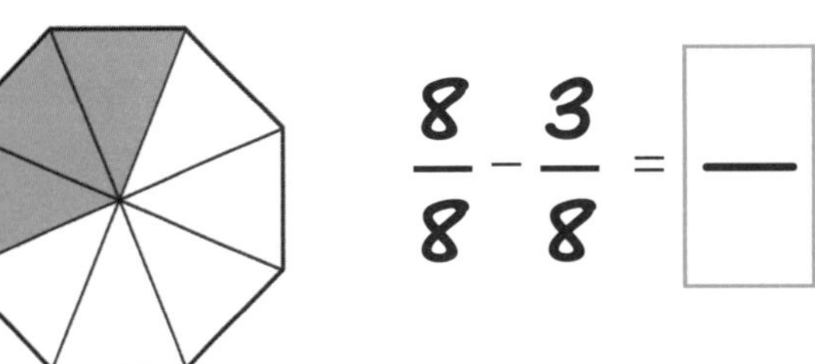

$\frac{8}{8} - \frac{3}{8} = \frac{\square}{\square}$

$\frac{10}{10} - \frac{6}{10} = \frac{\square}{\square}$

Tenths

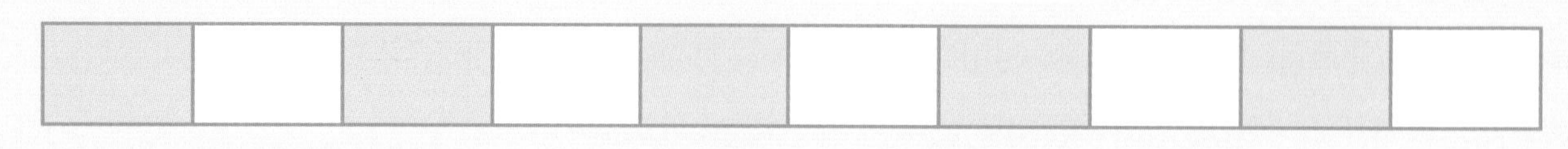

This shape is divided into ten $\frac{1}{10}$s. There are ten $\frac{1}{10}$s in 1 whole.

There are 10mm in 1cm. So 1mm is $\frac{1}{10}$ of 1cm.

There are 100p in £1. So 10p is $\frac{1}{10}$ of £1.

1. What fraction of each shape is shaded?

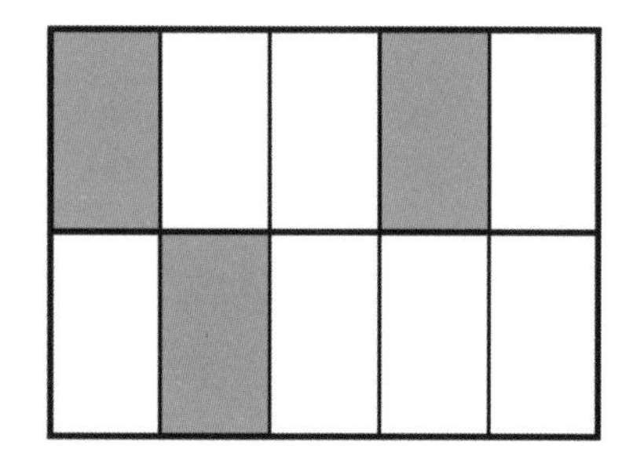

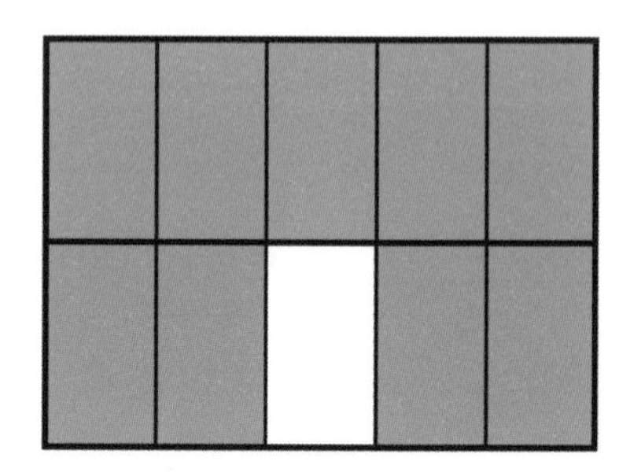

2. What fraction of each shape is shaded?

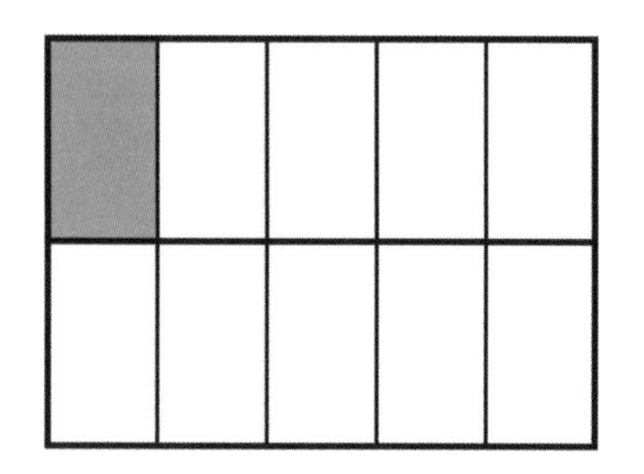

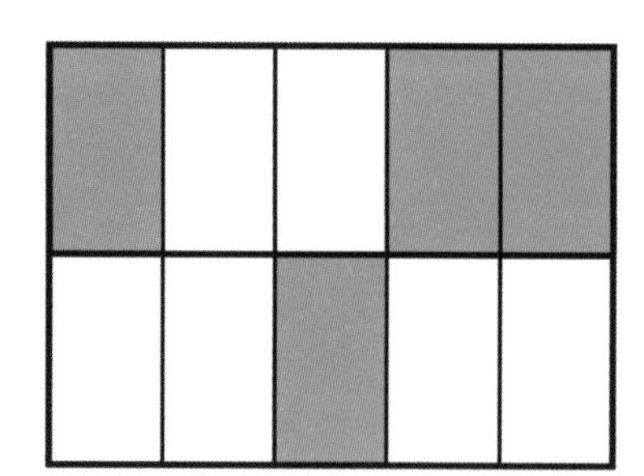

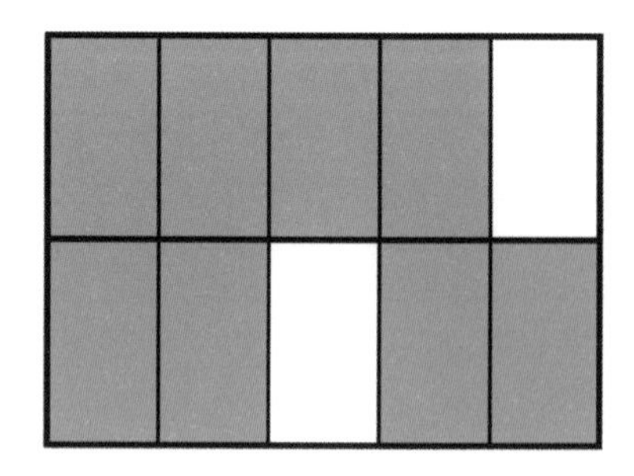

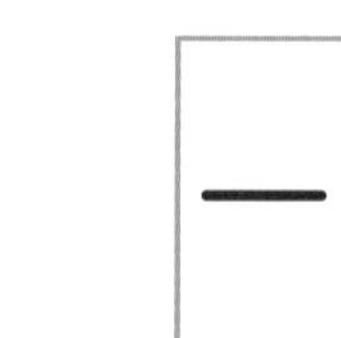

3. Fill in the missing tenths.

$\frac{1}{10}$		$\frac{3}{10}$	$\frac{4}{10}$			$\frac{7}{10}$			

Fraction word problems

To find a fraction of a number, divide the number by the denominator.

For example, $\frac{1}{3}$ of 30 is the same as 30 ÷ 3 = 10.

To find $\frac{2}{3}$ of 30 you just multiply $\frac{1}{3}$ by 2: $\frac{1}{3}$ = 10 so $\frac{2}{3}$ = 20.

1. Read each problem. Ask yourself: *Is it a one- or two-step problem?* Write a number sentence for the problem, then work out the answer. Write down your method.

Word problem	Method	Answer
Sally has 80p in her purse. She spends $\frac{3}{4}$ of her money on some sweets. How much does she spend?		
Paul has 45 marbles. He puts $\frac{2}{5}$ of the marbles in his pocket. How many are in his pocket?		
$\frac{2}{3}$ of the cakes at a party are eaten. There were 36 on the plate. How many are left?		
There is a plate of 36 pieces of fruit on the table. $\frac{1}{3}$ are bananas. $\frac{1}{4}$ are apples. All the rest are oranges. How many are oranges?		

Using a ruler

Practise using a ruler to measure different items. Make sure that the '0' on the ruler is lined up with the end of the item you are measuring. If the object is more than $8\frac{1}{2}$cm but not quite 9cm, then you round up the measurement to 9cm. If it is nearer to $8\frac{1}{2}$cm then you round down to $8\frac{1}{2}$cm.

1. You need a ruler marked in half centimetres. Measure the lines below (labelled a. to e.) as accurately as you can. Write down your measurements.

a.

b.

c.

d.

e.

2. Now draw these lines. Be as accurate as you can.

a. 5cm

b. 3cm

c. $7\frac{1}{2}$cm

d. $1\frac{1}{2}$cm

e. $3\frac{1}{2}$cm

10 centimetres

Estimate and measure lengths using centimetres and half centimetres. Make sure you line up the item to be measured with the '0' on the ruler, then take a reading. When estimating, look at 10cm carefully and then try and find items that are about that length.

1. **Find something at home that you estimate to be about 10cm long.**
   Now measure it as accurately as you can, to the nearest $\frac{1}{2}$cm use the ruler on the page to help you.
   Write your estimate and measurement in the table.
   Do this five more times.

I chose	My estimate	My measurement

0 1 2 3 4 5 6 7 8 9 10 11 12 13 14 15 16 17 18 19 20 cm

2. **Now find something that you estimate to be about 20cm in length. Measure it and write what you did here.**

____

____

____

____

____

Weighing things

A medium-sized potato weighs about 100g.

Use this fact to estimate the mass of other objects.

You could hold a potato in one hand and the other object in the other hand. Which feels heavier? How much heavier?

1. **Which do you think weighs more – a shoe or a jumper? Get one of each and estimate their mass in grams. Fill in your estimates on the chart below. Now weigh them, and check your estimates.**
2. **Try estimating the mass of some more pairs of objects and then check your estimates. Fill in the table.**

Object	Estimated mass	Mass in grams	Object	Estimated mass	Mass in grams
Shoe			Jumper		
Ruler			Scissors		
Mug			Plate		
Spoon			Fork		

3. **Choose 4 more pairs of objects. Estimate and then check their mass.**

Object	Estimated mass	Weight in grams	Object	Estimated mass	Mass in grams

Measuring capacity

Capacity is how much a container holds. We measure capacity in **millilitres (ml)** and **litres (l)**.

We use millilitres to measure the capacity of smaller containers.

We use litres to measure the capacity of larger containers.

Tip: 1000 millilitres is equivalent to 1 litre.

1. **Decide which unit of measurement to use when measuring the capacity of each of these containers. Tick the correct box.**

	Measure in litres	Measure in millilitres

Telling the time

Starting at 12 o'clock, practise counting round the clock in 5-minute intervals.

It is 25 minutes past 2 or 2.25.

Some clocks use Roman numerals instead of numbers.

1. Read the times on these clocks.

2. Write the time in digital time. The first one has been done for you.

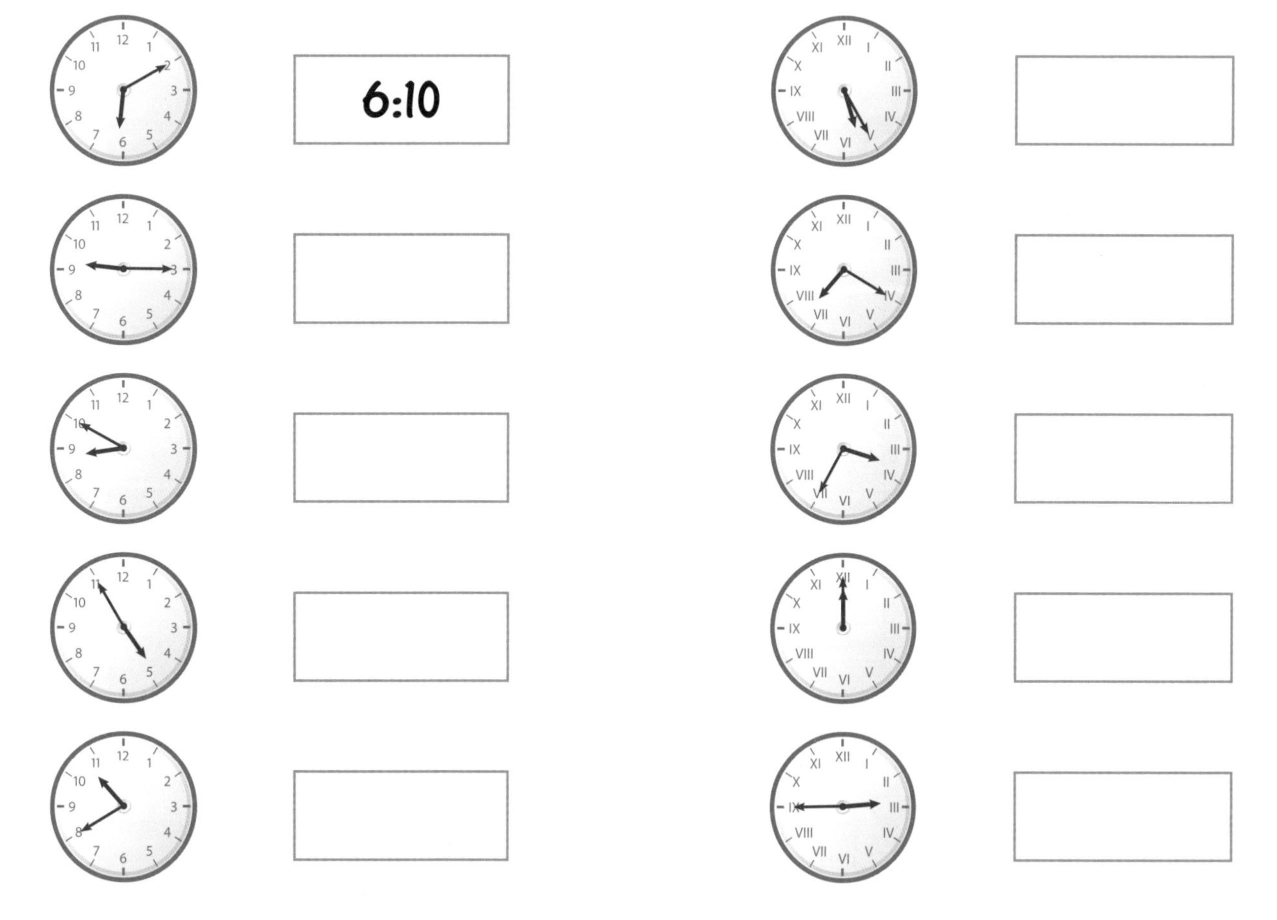

3. Now answer these questions.

a. What time do you get up in the morning? ______________________________

b. What time do you go to bed at night? ______________________________

c. So how long are you out of bed during the day? ______________________

TV times

You can use counting on to help you find time differences.

To find how long it is between 6:55 and 7:37, count in 5-minute intervals round the clock and then add on the extra 2 minutes, which makes 42 minutes.

1. Draw the hands on each clock to show the answer. Then write the time for each answer, saying if it is am or pm.

a. Trevor started watching Motor Racing at 6.30pm. The programme finished 42 minutes later. At what time did Motor Racing finish?

b. Trevor then watched Cook it! which ended 37 minutes before 9 o'clock in the evening. At what time did Cook it! end?

c. The news was on at 8 o'clock in the morning. Trevor woke up 28 minutes before it started. What time did he wake up?

d. Trevor woke up at 11.40pm. He watched Late Night Chat before going to bed. The programme started at ten past 12 and ended 26 minutes later. What time did it end?

Units of time

A second is a small unit of time. There are 60 seconds in 1 minute.

Try sitting still for a second. Now try sitting still for a minute – this will seem much longer!

1. **For each activity, ask someone to time you using a stopwatch or the second hand on a watch.**
2. **Before you start, write down your predictions.**
3. **Record your actual results.**

Activity	Prediction (seconds)	Time taken (seconds)
Write my name five times		
Tie my shoelace		
Put on my jacket		
Take off my shoes and socks		
Say the alphabet		

4. **Fill in the missing numbers. How many…**

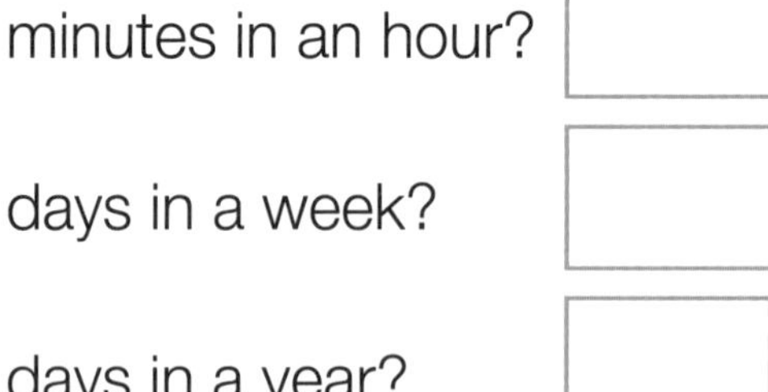

seconds in minute?		minutes in an hour?	
hours in a day?		days in a week?	
weeks in a year?		days in a year?	

5. **Draw a line to match each activity to the most sensible unit of time.**

Zip up a jacket	months
Go on holiday	years
Read a book	days
A school term	seconds
Growing from a child to an adult	hours

Money calculations

When solving money problems, you may find it useful to use real money.

You may also find that rounding the amounts up or down will help you solve the problems.

Yasmin wants to buy a present for everyone in her family. She has £10 to spend. She lives with her mother, father and brother, Ouni. Ouni is eight years old.

1. Help Yasmin decide what to buy.

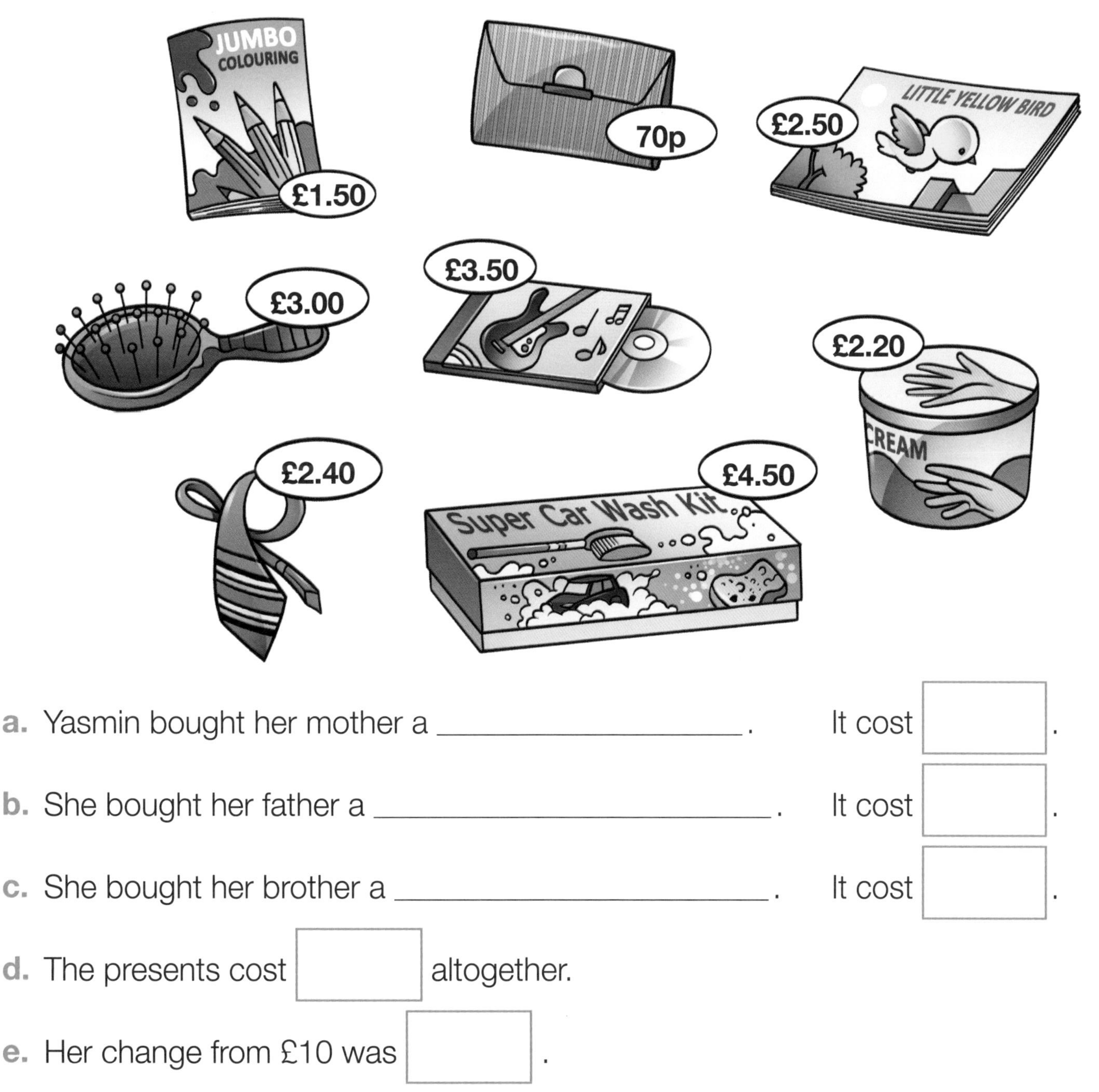

a. Yasmin bought her mother a ____________________. It cost ☐.

b. She bought her father a __________________________. It cost ☐.

c. She bought her brother a ________________________. It cost ☐.

d. The presents cost ☐ altogether.

e. Her change from £10 was ☐.

Sorting 2D shapes

Remember: A quadrilateral is any flat shape with four sides, such as a square or rectangle. A right angle is a square corner.

1. **Look carefully at each shape.**
2. **Read each shape description.**
3. **Draw a line from each shape to its description.**
4. **Write the shape's name in the space next to it.**

Shape	Description
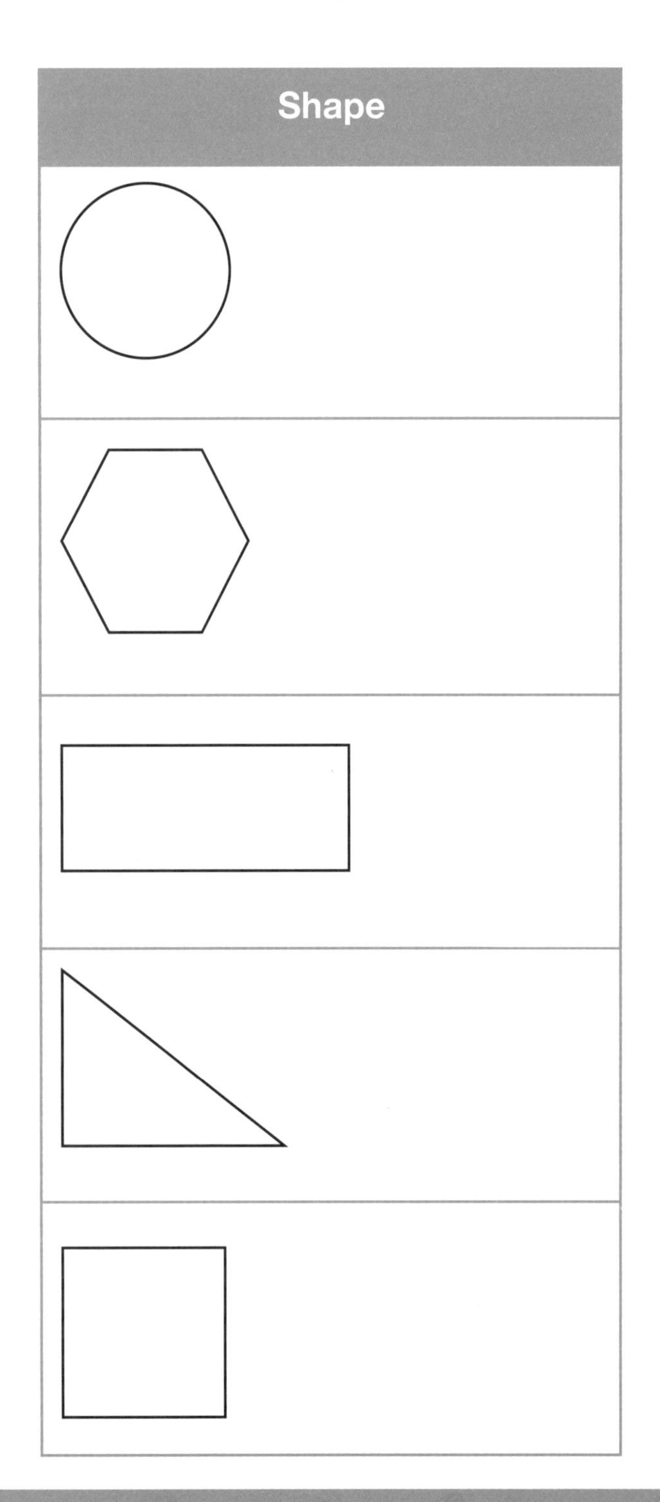	This shape has three sides. It has a right angle.
	This shape is a quadrilateral. All of its sides are the same length. All of its angles are the same size.
	This shape has no straight sides. It is symmetrical.
	This shape has angles all the same size. It has no right angles. It has six sides.
	This shape is not a square. It is a quadrilateral. It has four right angles.

Drawing 2D shapes

Read the descriptions below. Look around you to find shapes that match each description. Then draw them. For some shapes, you can use a ruler to help you.

1. Sketch three 2D shapes that have four right angles and opposite sides equal in length.

2. Sketch three shapes that have no right angles.

3D shape tree

A face is the flat surface of a 3D shape.

For example, a cube has six square faces.

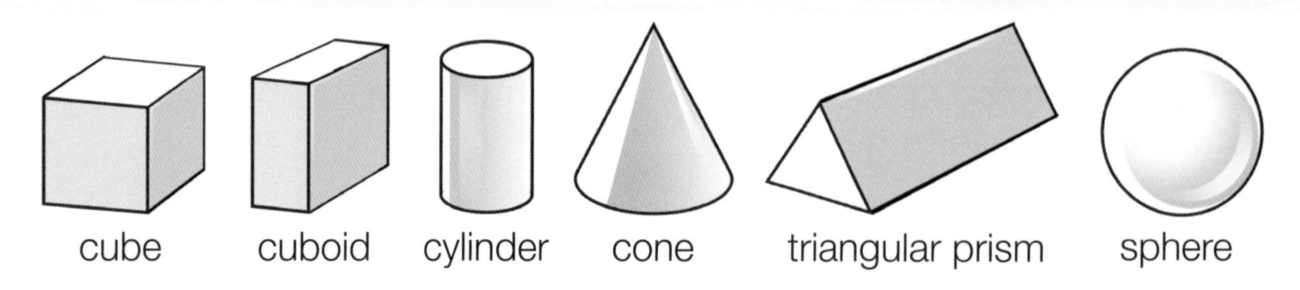

1. Complete the tree diagram using each of these 3D shapes in turn. Write the name of the shape in all of the appropriate places on the diagram. The first one has been done for you.

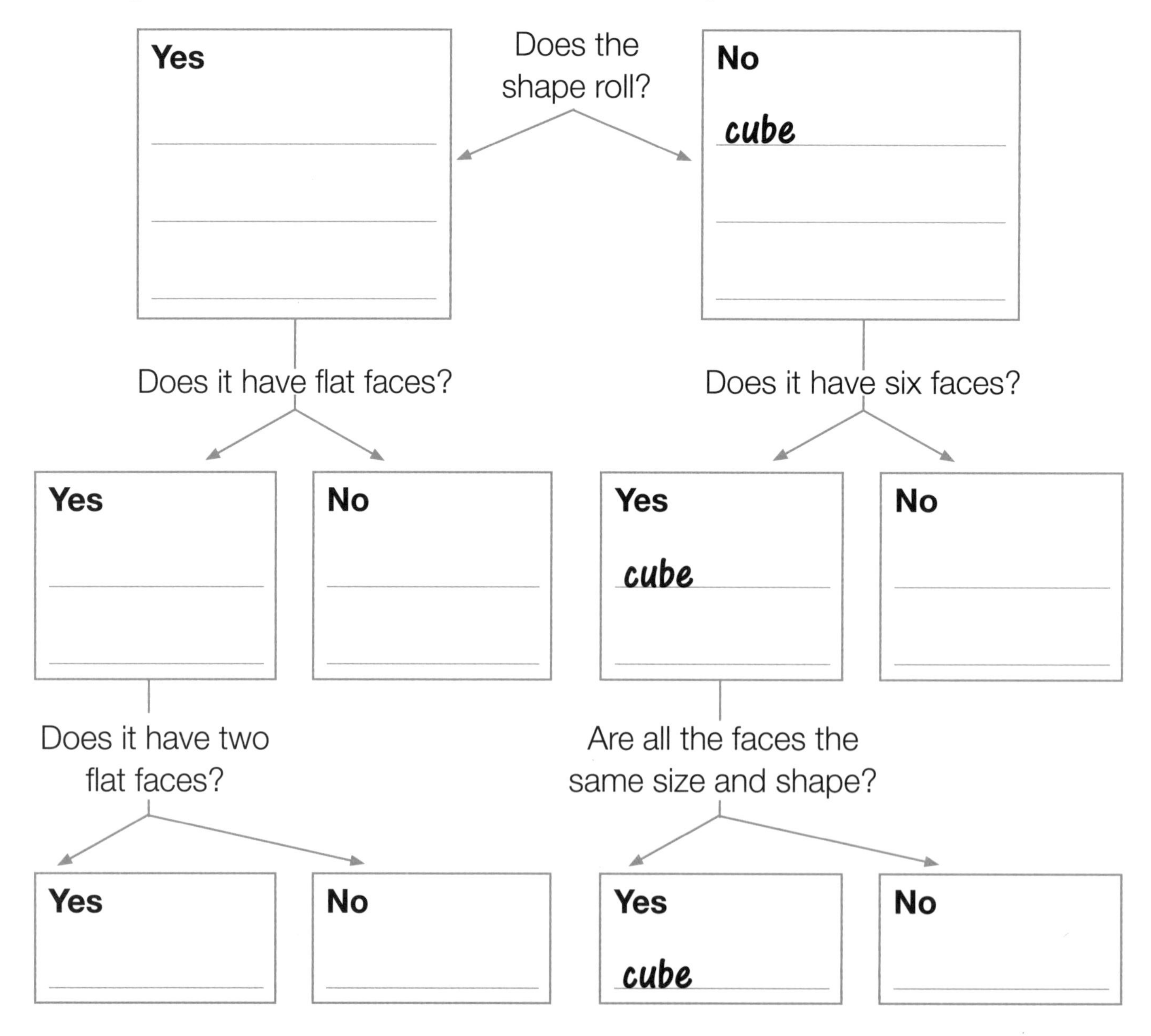

Lines

Read these words and their meanings to help you complete the activity below.

- Horizontal – parallel to the horizon.
- Vertical – at right angles to the horizon.
- Parallel – lines that stay the same distance apart.
- Perpendicular – lines that are at right angles to each other.

1. Mark each pair of parallel lines in a matching colour.

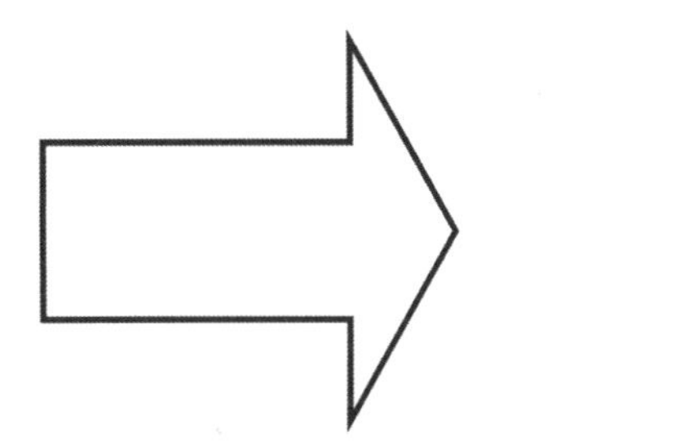

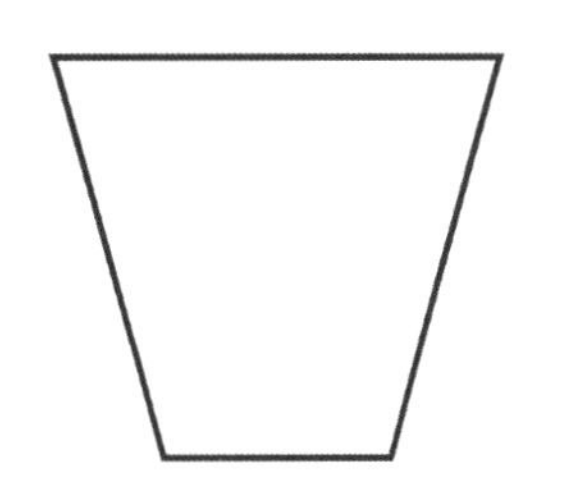

2. Which line is perpendicular to the line AB? Colour it red on each shape.

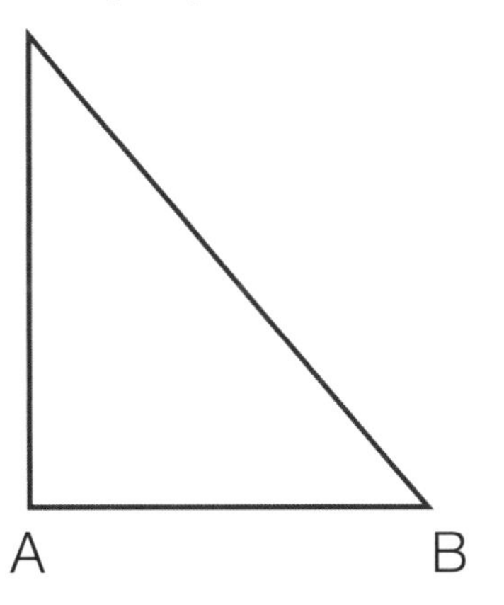

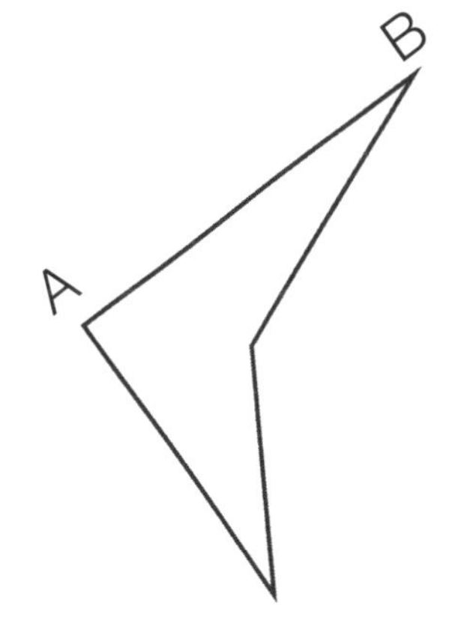

3. Write each label in the correct place.

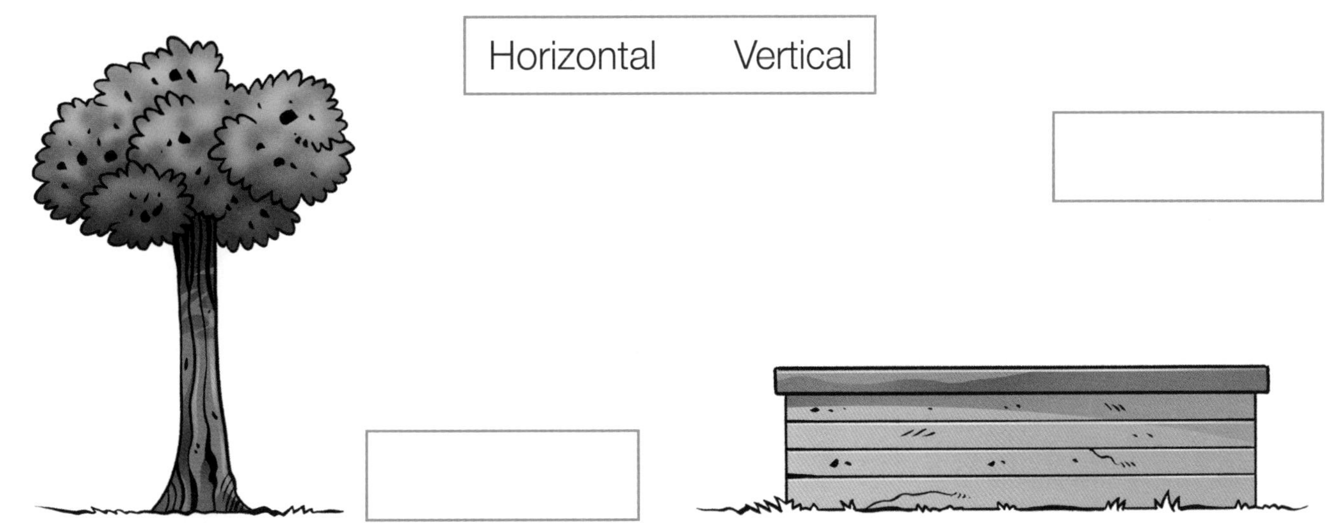

Is it a right angle?

Tear off one corner of a rectangular piece of paper. The corner is a right angle.

To test the angles below, put the pointed corner of your paper into the point of each angle.

Line up the sides. If it fits exactly, it is a right angle.

1. Mark all the right angles on these shapes with a square. □
2. Mark the angles that are smaller than a right angle with a less-than symbol. <
3. Mark the angles that are larger than a right angle with a more-than symbol. >

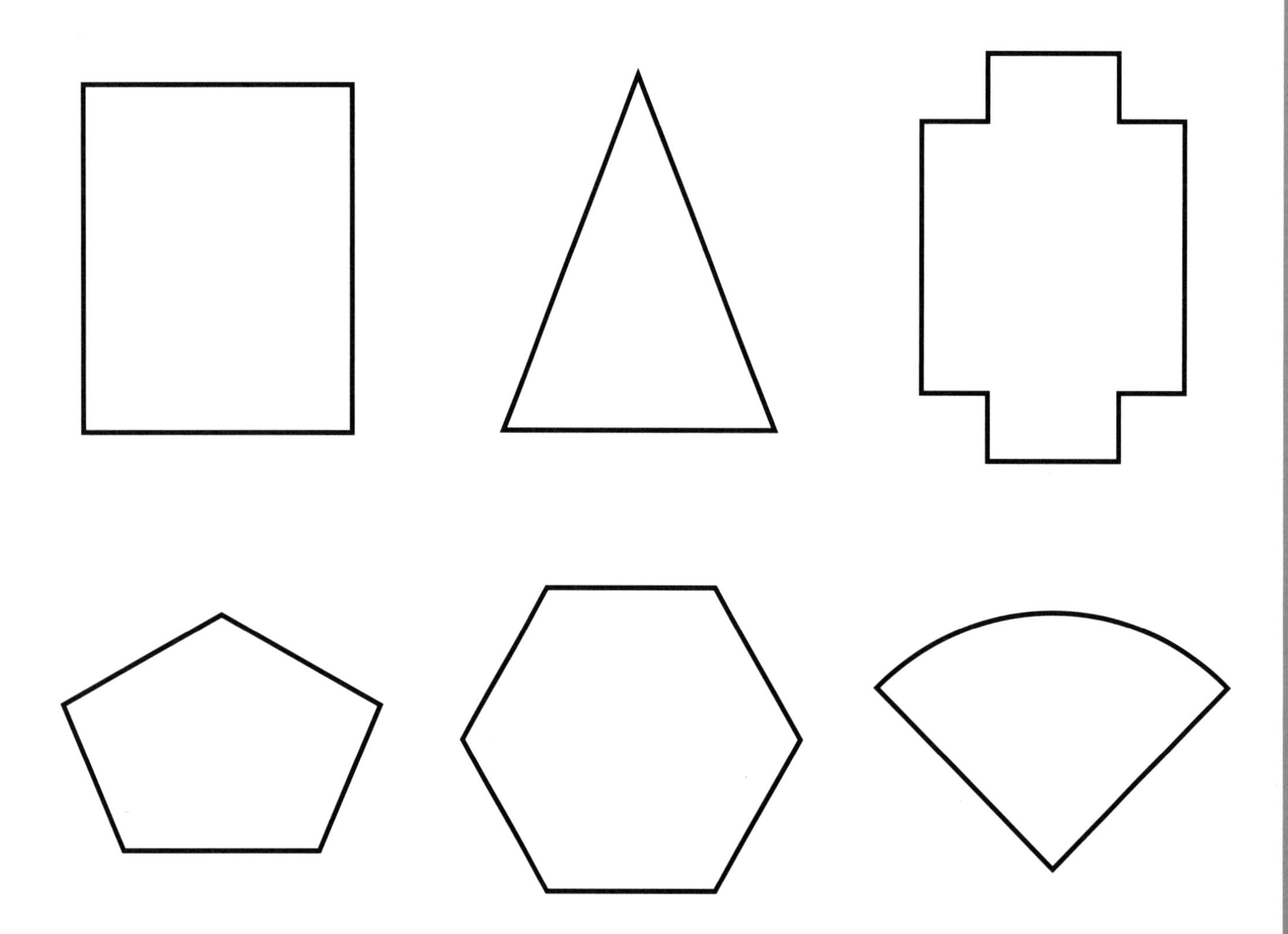

Acute, obtuse or right?

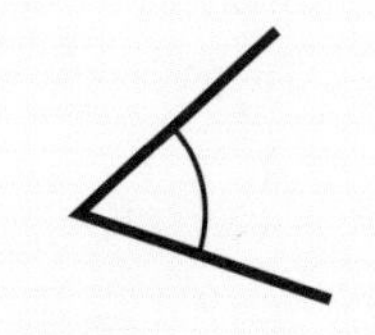

Acute angle: less than 90°

Right angle: 90°

Obtuse angle: more than 90°

1. Draw lines to match each angle to the correct label.

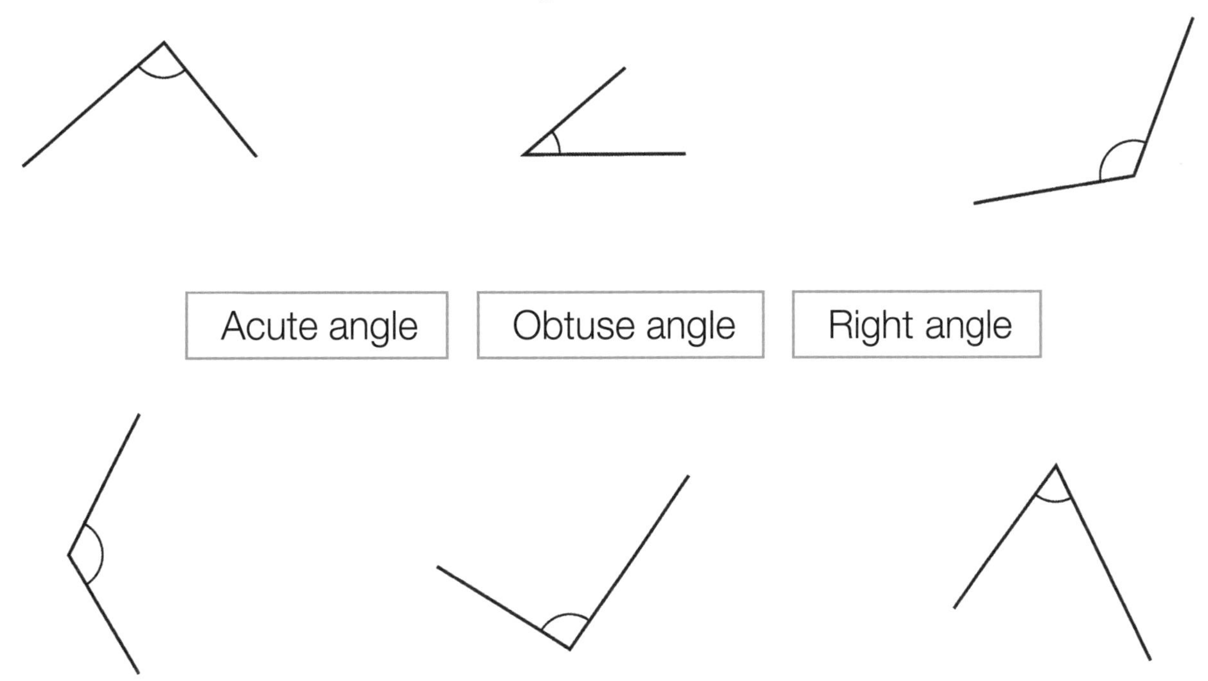

2. Colour in each angle of the shapes below using the colour code.

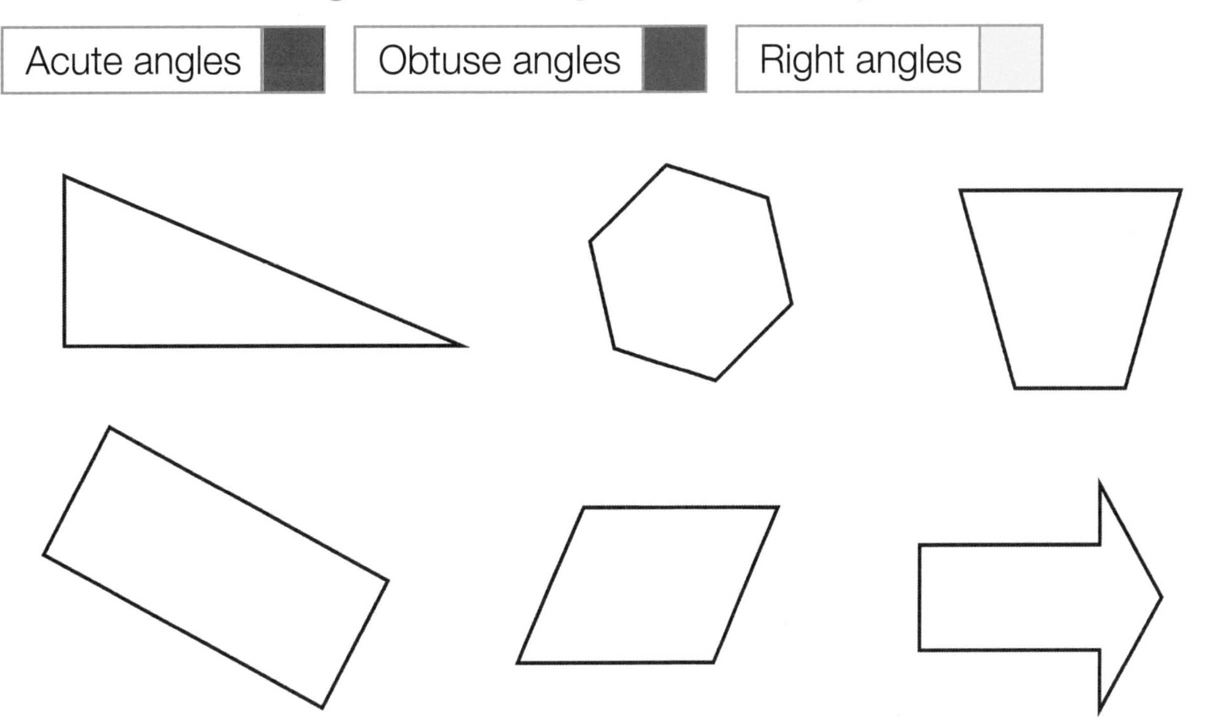

Frequency tables

We use **frequency tables** to present information and make it easier to understand.

Year 3 did a survey over five days. They wrote down the number of wild birds spotted in the playground between 10.30am and 11.00am each morning. This frequency table shows the results of Year 3's survey.

Day	Wild birds spotted
Monday	14
Tuesday	11
Wednesday	0
Thursday	16
Friday	12

1. Read the information in the table and use it to answer the questions below.

a. How many birds were spotted on Tuesday? ______________________

b. How many birds were spotted on Thursday and Friday in total?

____

c. On which day were the most birds spotted?

____

d. What was the total number of birds spotted over the five days?

____

e. Give one possible reason why no birds were spotted on Wednesday.

____

____

Pictograms

A **pictogram** is a graph that uses pictures or symbols to show information about how often something occurs.

Vince did a class survey about favourite types of console games. Here are the results of his survey:

- 6 children like platform games.
- 9 children prefer racing games.
- 3 children like puzzle games.
- 15 children say sports games are their favourite.

1. **Present Vince's results as a pictogram. A whole controller is equal to two children. You will need to divide the total number of children by two to work out how many whole and half controllers to draw for each type of console game. Try to make each controller the same size.**

- Use [whole controller] to show every two children.
- Use [half controller] to show one child.

Console game	Number of children
Platform	
Racing	
Puzzle	
Sports	

2. **Which is the least popular style of console game?** ____________

3. **Which is the most popular?** ____________

4. **How many children did Vince ask altogether?** ____________

Bar charts

A **bar chart** displays data using bars of the same width. Each bar represents a different category. The bar chart allows you to compare the items displayed.

Data can be displayed horizontally or vertically.

Use the information in the bar chart to answer the questions below.

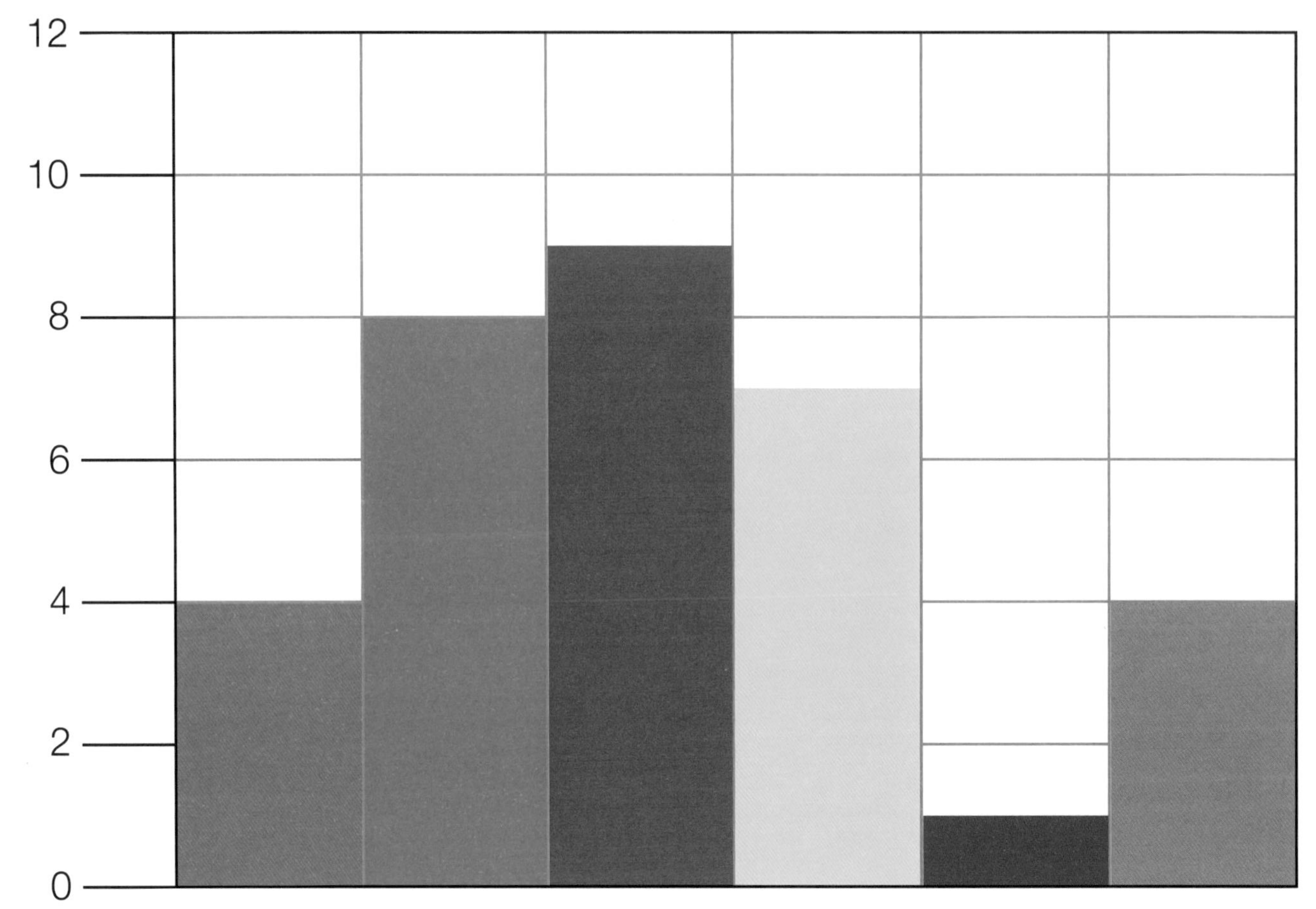

1. **How many more children like red than like purple?** ______________

2. **Which is the most popular colour?** ______________

3. **Every child in Year 3 decided on their favourite colour.**

   How many children are there in Year 3? ______________

4. **Which is the least popular colour?** ______________

5. **What is your favourite colour?** ______________

Make a bar chart

To make a bar chart, first give it a title. Then decide on a label for each axis, and where to put the information. Also decide on a scale for your chart.

A class did a survey to find out the favourite 'free-choice' activity of everyone in the class.

Building bricks	✗	✗	✗	✗	✗	✗	✗	✗
Painting	✗	✗	✗					
Console games	✗	✗	✗	✗	✗			
Reading	✗	✗	✗	✗	✗	✗		
Shop	✗	✗	✗	✗	✗			
Jigsaw puzzles	✗	✗	✗					

1. Make a bar chart to show the results of this class survey.

Title: ______________________

2. The children found out that building bricks were the favourite activity.

a. What activity was the second favourite? ______________________

b. How many children did they ask? ______________________

Progress chart

Making progress? Tick (✔) the flower boxes as you complete each section of the book.

Answers

The answers are given below. They are referenced by page number and where applicable, question number. The answers usually only include the information the children are expected to give.

Page number	Question number	Answers
6	1	One of the following, depending on start number chosen: 0, 3, 6, 9, 12, 15, 18, 21, 24, 27 1, 4, 7, 10, 13, 16, 19, 22, 25, 28 2, 5, 8, 11, 14, 17, 20, 23, 26, 29
	2	One of the following, depending on start number chosen: 0, 4, 8, 12, 16, 20, 24, 28, 32, 36 1, 5, 9, 13, 17, 21, 25, 29, 33, 37 2, 6, 10, 14, 18, 22, 26, 30, 34, 38 3, 7, 11, 15, 19, 23, 27, 31, 34, 39
	3	One of the following, depending on start number chosen: 0, 5, 10, 15, 20, 25, 30, 35, 40, 45 1, 6, 11, 16, 21, 26, 31, 36, 41, 46 2, 7, 12, 17, 22, 27, 32, 37, 42, 47 3, 8, 13, 18, 23, 28, 33, 38, 43, 48 4, 9, 14, 19, 24, 29, 34, 39, 44, 49
7	1a	290
	1b	1s are the same
	2a	577
	2b	1s are the same
	3a	253
	3b	1s are the same
	4a	648
	4b	100s change
	5a	956
	5b	100s change
	6a	45
	6b	100s change
8	1	

Number	100s	10s	1s
649	600	40	9
333	300	30	3
509	500	0	9
590	500	90	0
950	900	50	0
905	900	0	5
237	200	30	7

Page number	Question number	Answers
8	2	Answers will vary.
	3	Answers will vary.
9	1	16 + 8 = **24** 24 + 7 = **31** 16 + 18 = **34** 24 + 17 = **41** 16 + 28 = **44** 24 + 27 = **51** 93 – 7 = **86** 93 – 17 = **76** 93 – 27 = **66**
9	2	16 + **38** = **54** 93 – **37** = **56** 24 + **37** = **61** 16 + **48** = **64** 93 – **47** = **46** 24 + **47** = **71** 16 + **58** = **74** 93 – **57** = **36** 24 + **57** = **81** 16 + **68** = **84** 93 – **67** = **26** 24 + **67** = **91** 16 + **78** = **94** 93 – **77** = **16** 24 + **77** = **101** 16 + **88** = **104** 93 – **87** = **6** 24 + **87** = **111**

Page number	Question number	Answers
10	1	18 = 118 232 = 332 147 = 247 523 = 623
	2	

200 less	Starting number	200 more
162	362	562
559	759	959
394	594	794
631	831	1031

Page number	Question number	Answers
11	1a	156, 165, 516, 561, 615, 651
	1b	831, 879, 887, 897, 901, 910
	1c	497, 499, 500, 501, 504, 516
	2	Answers will vary. For example: 458, 548, 854
	3	Answers will vary based on question 2.
12	1a	963
	1b	369
	2a	752
	2b	257
	3a	976
	3b	235
13	1	Yes.
	2	2 × 30 is 60 and it is also an even number; 3 × 20 is 60; 4 × 15 is 60; 5 × 12 is 60 and it also ends in 0; 6 × 10 is 60; 10 × 6 is 60 and it also ends in 0.
14	1	Accept any suitable answer. Examples could include 14 + 3, 9 + 8, 12 + 5, 20 – 3, 20 – 3, 19 – 2
	2	1 + 19, 2 + 18, 3 + 17, 4 + 16, 5 + 15, 6 + 14, 7 + 13, 8 + 12, 9 + 11, 10 + 10 – accept numbers in either order.
15	1	8 + 92 = 100, 11 + 89 = 100, 15 + 85 = 100, 16 + 84 = 100, 22 + 78 = 100, 31 + 69 = 100, 36 + 64 = 100, 38 + 62= 100, 44 + 56 = 100, 49 + 51 = 100
	2a	33 stamps
	2b	28p
16	1a	81
	1b	37
	1c	152
	1d	17
	1e	171
	1f	35
	1g	180
	1h	88
	1i	237
	1j	245
17		Estimate: 80, Answer: 81 Estimate: 90, Answer: 93 Estimate: 70, Answer: 65 Estimate: 70, Answer: 71 Estimate: 50, Answer: 47

Page number	Question number	Answers
18	1a	65
	1b	50
	1c	40 57
	1d	57
19	1	333 623 377
20	1a	200 and 30 and 4 100 and 20 and 3 = 111
	1b	600 and 80 and 7 300 and 60 and 3 = 324
	1c	500 and 90 and 6 200 and 40 and 5 = 351
	1d	600 and 20 and 7 400 and 0 and 2 = 225
21	1	207, 374 149, 374
	2	326, 248 485, 356
22	1	3, 6, 9, 12, 15, 18, 21, 24, 27, 30, 33, 36, 39 Multiple of 3: 30, 33, 36, 39 Both: 3, 6, 9, 12, 15, 18, 21, 24, 27 Number less than 30: 1, 2, 4, 5, 7, 8, 10, 11, 13, 14, 16, 17, 19, 20, 22, 23, 25, 26, 28, 29
	2	4, 8, 12, 16, 20, 24, 28, 32, 36, 40, 44, 48 Multiple of 4: 32, 36, 40, 44, 48 Both: 4, 8, 12, 16, 20, 24, 28 Number less than 30: 1, 2, 3, 5, 6, 7, 9, 10, 11, 13, 14, 15, 17, 18, 19, 21, 22, 23, 25, 26, 27, 29
23	4	(see table below)

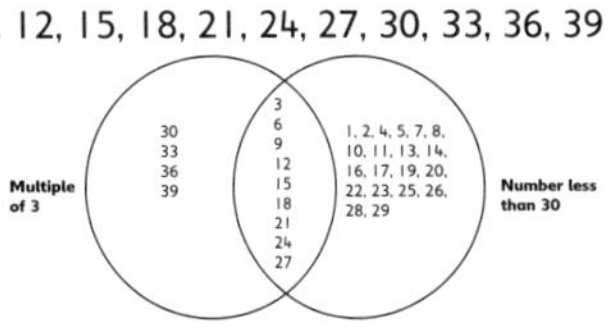

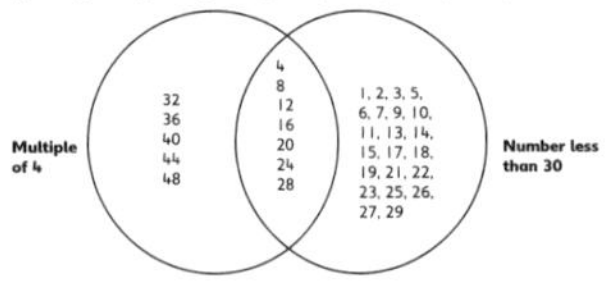

	Multiple of 4	Not a multiple of 4
Multiple of 3	12, 24, 36	3, 6, 9, 15, 18, 21, 27, 30, 33, 39
Not a multiple of 3	4, 8, 16, 20, 28, 32, 40	1, 2, 5, 7, 10, 11, 13, 14, 17, 19, 22, 23, 25, 26, 29, 31, 34, 35, 37, 38

Page number	Question number	Answers
24	1a	48
	1b	72
	1c	32
	1d	24
	1e	64
	1f	16
	1g	80
24	2	48 legs = 6 spiders 64 legs = 8 spiders 32 legs = 4 spiders 80 legs = 10 spiders 16 legs = 2 spiders
	3	even
25	1a	eight, eight
	1b	3, 3
	1c	28, 4
	1d	thirty-two, thirty-two
	2a	7, 21, 21
	2b	8, 16, 2
	2c	60, 10, 6
	3	7 × 5 = 35 35 ÷ 7 = 5 5 × 7 = 35 35 ÷ 5 = 7

Page number	Question number	Answers
26	1–4	Answers will vary. Examples could include:

Grid number	Row number	Number sentence	Jottings	Answer
11	3	11 × 5	10 × 5 (50) and 1 × 5 (5)	55
16	6	16 × 6	10 × 6 (60) and 6 × 6 (36)	96
13	4	13 × 4	10 × 4 (40) and 3 × 4 (12)	52

Page number	Question number	Answers
27	1a	43 × 2 = 86
	1b	23 × 2 = 46
	1c	24 × 3 = 72
	1d	48 × 2 = 96
	1e	14 × 3 = 42
	1f	26 × 4 = 104
28	1a	64
	1b	165
	1c	192
	1d	225
	1e	124
	1f	288
	1g	320
	1h	261
29	1a	24 ÷ 3 = 8
	1b	30 ÷ 5 = 6
	1c	14 ÷ 2 = 7
	1d	24 ÷ 4 = 6
	1e	30 ÷ 10 = 3
30	1a	6
	1b	5
	1c	7
	1d	4
	1e	13
	1f	9
	1g	7
	1h	12
	1i	9
	2a	eight groups
	2b	eight
	2c	nine
	3a	4cm
	3b	3 hours
	3c	10km
	3d	9g
	3e	£12
	3f	2kg
31	1a	21
	1b	15
	1c	32
	1d	15
	1e	24
	1f	17
	1g	19
	1h	36

Page number	Question number	Answers
32–33	1	60 ÷ 5 = 12 35 × 3 = 105 75 ÷ 5 = 15 64 × 5 = 320
	2	5 × 14 = 70 12 + 14 = 26 ÷ 6 = 4 remainder 2; Answer: 4 boxes 64 ÷ 2 = 32 ÷ 2 = 16; Answer: 16 chocolate flakes 25 + 20 = 45 ÷ 6 = 7 remainder 3; Answer; 8 cartons
34	1	$\frac{1}{8}$ $\frac{1}{10}$ $\frac{1}{3}$ $\frac{1}{4}$ $\frac{1}{2}$
35	1	$\frac{3}{8}$ $\frac{2}{3}$ $\frac{3}{4}$ $\frac{3}{5}$
	2	14 balls, 8 cars, 15 sweets
	3a	75cm
	3b	240g
	3c	100ml
36	1	Shape / Simple fraction / Equivalent fraction: Triangles: $\frac{3}{24}$, $\frac{1}{8}$ Squares: $\frac{9}{24}$, $\frac{3}{8}$ Circles: $\frac{8}{24}$, $\frac{1}{3}$ Pentagons: $\frac{4}{24}$, $\frac{1}{6}$ Triangles and squares: $\frac{12}{24}$, $\frac{1}{2}$
	2	$\frac{1}{2} = \frac{3}{6} = \frac{12}{24} = \frac{5}{10}$ $\frac{1}{4} = \frac{2}{8} = \frac{5}{20} = \frac{4}{16}$
37	1–2	$\frac{1}{2} = \frac{2}{4}$ $\frac{2}{8} = \frac{1}{4}$ $\frac{4}{10} = \frac{2}{5}$ $\frac{4}{6} = \frac{2}{3}$ $\frac{8}{10} = \frac{4}{5}$ $\frac{5}{10} = \frac{1}{2}$ Answers will vary for comparison fractions.
38	1a–c	0, $\frac{1}{8}$, $\frac{1}{4}$, $\frac{1}{2}$, 1 0, $\frac{1}{6}$, $\frac{1}{3}$, $\frac{2}{3}$, $\frac{5}{6}$, 1 0, $\frac{1}{8}$, $\frac{1}{4}$, $\frac{3}{8}$, $\frac{7}{8}$, 1
	2	Answers will vary.
	3	Answers will vary based on question 2.

Page number	Question number	Answers
39	1	$\frac{1}{3} + \frac{1}{3} = \frac{2}{3}$ $\frac{3}{8} + \frac{2}{8} = \frac{5}{8}$ $\frac{2}{6} + \frac{1}{6} = \frac{3}{6}$ $\frac{3}{10} + \frac{4}{10} = \frac{7}{10}$ $\frac{2}{5} + \frac{1}{5} = \frac{3}{5}$
	2	$\frac{6}{6} - \frac{5}{6} = \frac{1}{6}$ $\frac{10}{10} - \frac{6}{10} = \frac{4}{10}$ $\frac{8}{8} - \frac{3}{8} = \frac{5}{8}$
40	1	$\frac{3}{10}, \frac{7}{10}, \frac{9}{10}$
	2	$\frac{1}{10}, \frac{4}{10}, \frac{8}{10}$
	3	$\frac{2}{10}, \frac{5}{10}, \frac{6}{10}, \frac{8}{10}, \frac{9}{10}, \frac{10}{10}$
41	1	60p 18 marbles 12 cakes 15 oranges
42	1a	6cm
	1b	7.5cm
	1c	4.5cm
	1d	8cm
	1e	2cm
	2a	Check accuracy with ruler.
	2b	Check accuracy with ruler.
	2c	Check accuracy with ruler.
	2d	Check accuracy with ruler.
	2e	Check accuracy with ruler.
43	1	Answers will vary.
	2	Answers will vary.
44	2	Answers will vary.
	3	Answers will vary.
45	1	Car – measure in litres Drink – measure in millilitres Bath – measure in litres Milk on cereal – measure in millilitres
46	1–2	6:10, 5:25 9:15, 7:20 8:50, 3:35 4:55, 12:00 10:40, 2:45
	3a	Answers will vary.
	3b	Answers will vary.
	3c	Answers will vary.
47	1a	7:12pm
	1b	8:23pm
	1c	7:32am
	1d	12:36am

Page number	Question number	Answers
48	1–3	Answers will vary.
	4	60 seconds in a minute; 60 minutes in an hour 24 hours in a day; 7 days in a week 52 weeks in a year; 365 days in a year
	5	Zip up a jacket = seconds Go on holiday = days Read a book = days A school term = weeks Growing from a child to an adult = years
49	1a	Answers will vary.
	1b	Answers will vary.
	1c	Answers will vary.
	1d	Answers will depend on answers 1a – 1c.
	1e	Answers will depend on answer 1d.
50	1–4	**Shape** This shape has no straight sides and is symmetrical. This shape has angles all the same size. It has no right angles. It has six sides This shape is not a square. It is a quadrilateral. It has four right angles. This shape has three sides. It has a right angle. This shape is a quadrilateral. All of its sides are the same length. All of its angles are the same size.
51	1	Children should have drawn three different rectangles and/or squares.
	2	Answers will vary.
52	1–2	Does the shape roll? Yes: cylinder, cone, sphere — No: cube, cuboid, triangular prism Does it have flat faces? Yes: cylinder, cone — No: sphere Does it have six faces? Yes: cube — No: triangular prism Does it have two flat faces? Yes: cylinder — No: cone Are all the faces the same size and shape? Yes: cube — No: cuboid
53	1	
	2	A B A B
	3	Tree = Vertical Fence = Horizontal

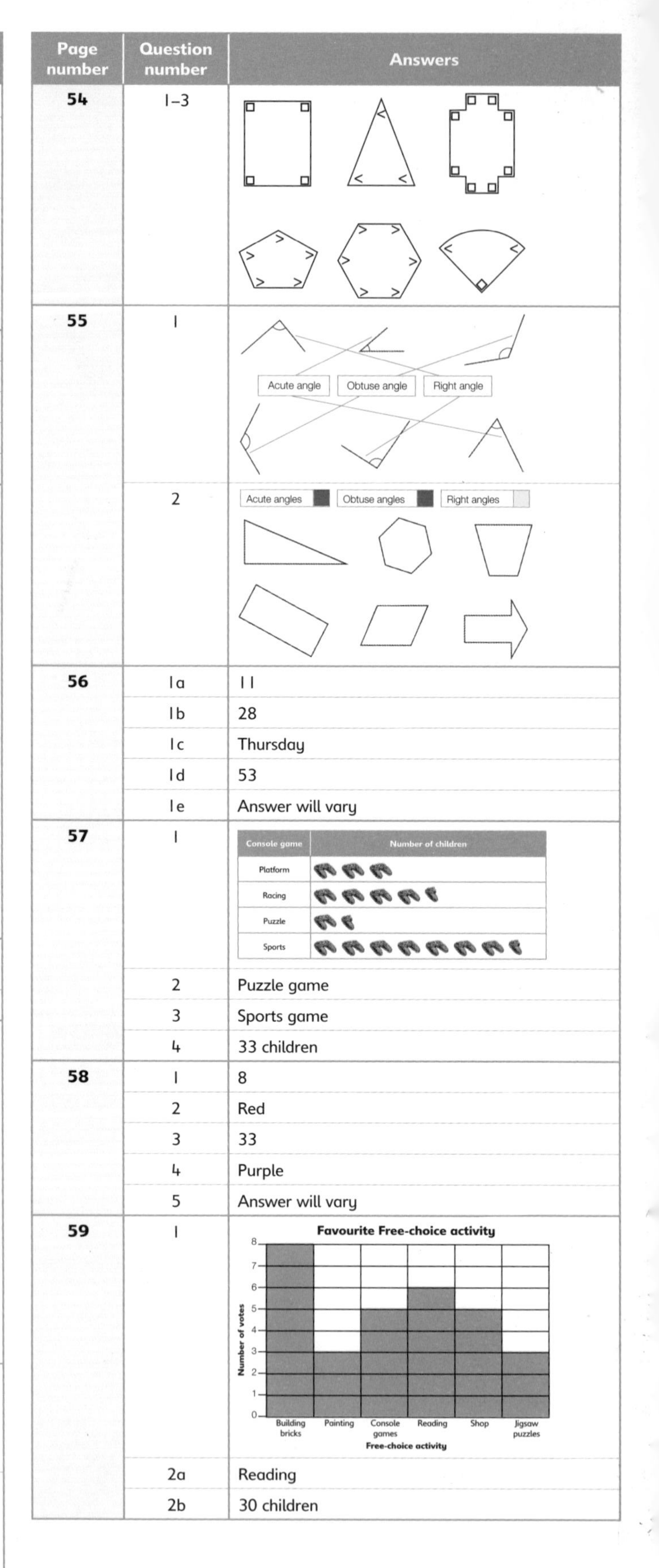

Page number	Question number	Answers
54	1–3	
55	1	Acute angle / Obtuse angle / Right angle
	2	Acute angles / Obtuse angles / Right angles
56	1a	11
	1b	28
	1c	Thursday
	1d	53
	1e	Answer will vary
57	1	Console game / Number of children Platform Racing Puzzle Sports
	2	Puzzle game
	3	Sports game
	4	33 children
58	1	8
	2	Red
	3	33
	4	Purple
	5	Answer will vary
59	1	**Favourite Free-choice activity** Number of votes: 0 1 2 3 4 5 6 7 8 Building bricks, Painting, Console games, Reading, Shop, Jigsaw puzzles Free-choice activity
	2a	Reading
	2b	30 children